D0458571

P7-CGX-328

TRANSLOCATION IN PLANTS

These Studies are designed to inform the mature student—the undergraduate upperclassman and the beginning graduate student—of the outstanding advances made in various areas of modern biology. The books will not be treatises but rather will briefly summarize significant information in a given field and interpret it in terms of our current knowledge of the rapidly expanding research findings within the life sciences. Also it is hoped that the Studies will be of interest to teachers and research workers.

BIOLOGY STUDIES

Bell, *The Biology of Sound*
Carlquist, *Comparative Plant Anatomy*
Crafts, *Translocation in Plants*
Deevey, *Historical Ecology*
Delevoryas, *Morphology and Evolution of Fossil Plants*
Hillman, *The Physiology of Flowering*
Slobodkin, *Growth and Regulation of Animal Populations*
Sutton, *Genes, Enzymes, and Inherited Diseases*

A. S. Crafts
University of California
Davis

TRANSLOCATION IN PLANTS

Holt, Rinehart and Winston
New York

This volume is
dedicated to

Dr. J. P. Bennett

Professor Emeritus,
University of California, Berkeley

LIBRARY OF CONGRESS CATALOG CARD NUMBER: 61-7852

21593-0111

PRINTED IN THE UNITED STATES OF AMERICA

preface

The problems of the translocation of solutes and water in plants were some of the first to be attacked by plant physiologists, and they have been some of the last to receive thorough and capable investigation. There is controversy, still, over many aspects, and no unanimity of opinion on any of the basic mechanisms.

There are several reasons for this unsatisfactory state. As mentioned in the introductory part of this volume, early work was influenced by the search for a circulating system in plants comparable with that in animals. Later work was often weakened by a lack of appreciation, on the part of physiologists, for the structure of vascular tissues. Even today, with modern tools at our disposal, translocation problems often appear deceptively simple when in fact they are very complex. Many investigators attack these problems with little background in the subject, with no understanding of the limits imposed on the mechanisms concerned by the anatomy of the tissues, and with little appreciation of the actual physical processes involved.

Despite the obviously unsatisfactory state of our understanding of translocation mechanisms, some of the studies made within the past three decades should go a long way toward providing answers. Whereas much of the early work involved ringing, grafting, and other manipulation of the experimental plants, work on virus movement by Bennett, Esau, and others has provided much solid evidence for movement of viruses with assimilates in whole, quite normal plants.

More recently, work with aphids and other phloem-feeding insects has confirmed the virus studies and has provided samples of phloem sap, obtained from insect mouth parts, in sufficient quan-

tity to make chemical and chromatographic analyses possible. The observation that this exudation continues for many hours is mute evidence for the fact that it comes from relatively normal phloem, since we know from the evidence of the many older studies on phloem exudation from cut stems or bark that injured phloem is soon plugged.

Use of radioactive isotopes has proved even more effective, in that translocation studies may be carried out on intact plants. Many labeled molecules will diffuse through the cuticle, migrate to the phloem, and move to remote plant parts in measurable quantities without causing any detectable disturbance of the plant. Use of $C^{14}O_2$ has proved particularly critical in such studies, for it is rapidly incorporated into assimilates that can be traced in several ways.

To the writer the symplast concept has been most useful in interpreting the results of translocation studies. Some tracers enter the symplast readily, migrate to the phloem, and thence move to remote plant parts at rapid rates; others seem unable to enter the symplast of leaves but move with relative ease in the contrasting nonliving apoplast phase; and some can apparently move readily in either system and actually migrate from one to the other. Thus phosphorus, for example, may enter roots, move into the xylem, translocate to the top of the plant via the apoplast, enter the symplast of the leaf, and move via the phloem back into the root where it may again leak into the xylem and reascend the stem. This is actually a circulation, though of a very different sort than that sought by early plant physiologists.

Equally useful have been the ideas that the lumina of the sieve tubes constitute a highly specialized phase of the symplast through which the assimilate stream moves at linear rates up to and above 100 cm per hour, and that the lumina of the tracheary elements of the xylem constitute a highly specialized phase of the apoplast system through which the transpiration stream commonly moves at even higher linear rates. Thus the plant may be visualized as made up of the symplast (the continuum of living stuff in which all life processes take place), the apoplast (the continuum of nonliving cell-wall material that surrounds and contains the symplast), and the intercellular gas phase. Water in the plant body constitutes a continuum that interpenetrates the symplast and the apoplast, and its movement is a complex resultant of hydrostatic, osmotic, and adsorptive forces. The great bulk of water that enters the plant from the soil moves to the foliar organs in the transpiration stream and is lost to the atmosphere as vapor; a small amount may move secondarily in the assimilate stream to the roots and thus circulate; an even smaller amount is held by osmotic and adsorptive forces in cells and cell walls; and even less is incorporated chemically into carbohydrates and so enters into the composition of the plant body.

A fact often overlooked is that the phloem and xylem are not mere systems of tubular conduits; they are distribution systems engaged in providing essential materials to every living cell of the plant. And the actual conduits are completely surrounded by living cells that move water and solutes into and out of the conduits. To attempt a mathematical analysis of the function of such systems seems to the writer to be the height of futility.

Although the realities of the structure and function of vascular plant tissues are thus very complex, plant physiologists must nevertheless continue their study, for not only do they constitute a great challenge but they must eventually provide answers to many pressing questions. The growth and nutrition of all plants depend upon these distribution systems. The movement of viruses, foliar-applied nutrients, and systemic pesticides is carried out by the vascular tissues, and the distribution and localization of natural plant constituents that characterize all plant species are a function of the conducting channels of these species. Only after we have obtained a clear picture of the functioning of these two distribution systems can we hope to understand how the living plant carries on its many processes of growth and dry-weight production.

The writer would like to express here his gratitude to his colleagues in the Botany Department at Davis and to co-workers in this and other countries who, by consultation, advice, and friendly criticism have served to formulate and crystallize the concepts put forth in this volume.

A. S. C.

Davis, California
March, 1961

contents

chapter one Introduction

Studies on the movement of materials into and around plants have been fraught with great difficulties. Starting with the early horticultural practices of ringing, grafting, and pruning in various ways, the first plant physiologists attempted to determine if sap in plants circulated as does blood in animals. Information accumulated slowly from piecemeal bits of experimental evidence and theories often preceded the confirming research.

Opinions fluctuated between physical explanations and vital theories. Water, at one time, was supposed to enter plants by diffusion, later by endosmosis, and even later by the pulsations of living cells. The rise of sap in tall trees was explained by capillarity, by gas pressure, by imbibition, by vital pumping, and finally by the cohesion mechanism.

Translocation of assimilates was pictured as taking place in the phloem promoted by diffusion, by protoplasmic streaming, by changing turgidity, by attaining equilibrium on the surface of the protoplasm, and by mass flow along a gradient of hydrostatic pressure.

At one time movement of both water and solutes was pictured as taking place in both directions in the xylem; at about the same time others pictured solute movement as taking place in both directions in the phloem.

Probably in no part of the field of plant physiology have so many theories been proved wrong, so many experiments obviously been misinterpreted, and so little solid evidence presented. This is not difficult to understand because translocation is a function of the whole, intact living plant, and as soon as one disturbs the plant in any way the processes of translocation are affected. Furthermore, these processes go on inside living tissues that are buried inside the plant body and are therefore difficult to measure. For this reason the experimenter must build his picture largely on surmise and circumstantial evidence. And so from a vast body of experimental evidence one is forced to glean a bit here and a particle there, always being on the lookout for uncritical technics and poorly founded explanations.

A more hopeful aspect of this problem is the work on virus movement. Virus—for example, curly top of sugar beets—is inoculated into the phloem of the host plant by the beet-leaf hopper and moved from the point of inoculation to other regions of the plant via the phloem. A large body of evidence indicates that such movement parallels food movement in the plant and that alterations in the pattern of movement can be brought about by proper manipulation of the host plant. This work has been reviewed (Crafts, 1939b; Bennett, 1940a; Crafts, 1951). It suffices here to point out that phloem-limited viruses such as curly top apparently accompany foods in the plant and follow a source-sink distribution pattern that can logically be explained only on a correlated movement of virus and assimilates as in a stream. Evidence for such distribution is damaging to any theory that postulates independent movement of individual molecules.

Although for many years the viruses alone served as ideal translocation indicators, the picture has changed in recent years. The discovery of synthetic hormonelike materials such as 2,4-D that will penetrate the surface of the leaf, migrate to the phloem, and translocate with endogenous assimilates has given us tools for studying intact plants. An example is the bean-bending test as used by Mitchell and Brown (1946), Weaver and De Rose (1946), Linder, Brown and Mitchell (1949), Rohrbaugh and Rice (1949), Weintraub and Brown (1950), and Day (1952).

The labeling of 2,4-D by incorporation of C^{14} in the molecule has provided an even better translocation indicator because now one can apply this compound at very low dosage, allow it time for movement, kill the plant with solid CO_2, freeze dry it to prevent further changes, and prepare autoradiographs that give an accurate and detailed picture of distribution of the tracer. Many other labeled compounds are now available for translocation studies (Crafts, 1959) allowing one to make comparative studies. After autoradiographing, the experimental plants may be fractionated, extracted, and chromatographed to detect changes that have occurred in the tracer during its uptake and distribution.

It is this latter situation that has prompted the writer to attempt the present treatise. The rapid advances made in the last decade indicate a possible break-through comparable with the discoveries of Dixon and Joly (1894) for xylem transport. However, although the prospects for a solution of the problem of phloem transport seem unusually hopeful at the present time, there is still one hurdle that must be surmounted: the permeability of the sieve plate and the mechanism by which it conducts as freely as it does. The writer has one suggestion, Dr. Spanner of the University of London (1958) has another; others will undoubtedly be made in the near future.

SECTION ONE

Review of Literature

chapter two

Movement of Water, Salts, and Assimilates

MOVEMENT OF WATER AND SALTS

To be comprehensive, any treatment of the movement of materials in plants must start with the discovery of the circulation of blood in the animal body by William Harvey in 1616, for this discovery not only ushered in a new era of progress in animal physiology; it flavored experimental work in plant physiology for over 200 years.

Ringing was an old horticultural practice and early ideas concerning the movement of nutrients in plants resulted from ringing experiments. Marcellus Malpighi (1675, 1679), the famous anatomist, ringed a great many plants throughout the year and he concluded that nutrient sap flows both upward and downward in stems through vessels occurring in both wood and bark. He failed to correlate the typical swelling above a ring with stoppage of downward movement but he noted that it occurred only during the active growing season of the plant.

Stephen Hales (1726) attempted to answer the question as to the possible circulation of sap in plants. Chapter IV of his *Vegetable Staticks,* Hales entitles "Experiments showing the ready lateral motion of the sap, and consequently the lateral communication of the sap-vessels. The free passage of it from the small branches towards the stem, as well as from the stem to the branches. With an account of some experiments, relating to the circulation or non-circulation of the sap." After describing some seven critical experiments Hales states, "We see in many of the foregoing experiments, what quantities of moisture trees do daily imbibe and perspire: now the celerity of the sap must be very great, if that quantity of moisture must, most of it, ascend to the top of the tree, then descend, and ascend again, before it is carried off by perspiration."

"The defect of a circulation in vegetables seems in some measure to be supplied by the much greater quantity of liquor, which the vegetable takes in, than the animal, whereby its motion is accelerated; for by Experiment 1, we find the sunflower, bulk for bulk, imbibes and perspires seventeen times more fresh liquor than a man, every 24 hours."

"Besides, nature's great aim in vegetables being only that the vegetable life be carried on and maintained, there was no occasion to give its sap the rapid motion which was necessary for the blood of animals."

Hales argues further, "The instance of the ilex grafted upon the English oak, seems to afford a very considerable argument against circulation. For if there were a free uniform circulation of the sap through the oak and ilex, why should the leaves of the oak fall in winter, and not those of the ilex?"

He concludes, "Upon the whole, I think we have, from these experiments and observations, sufficient ground to believe, that there is no circulation of sap in vegetables; notwithstanding many ingenious persons have been induced to think there was, from several curious observations and experiments, which evidently prove, that the sap does in some measure recede from the top towards the lower parts of plants, whence they were with good probability of reason induced to think that the sap circulated."

Hales also performed ringing experiments, finding that swelling above a ring occurred if leaves were present, but did not in portions isolated by rings and having no leaves. He attributed the swelling not to hindrance of downward movement of sap, but to enhanced nutrition resulting from the ability of leaves to draw sap from the surrounding tissues.

Knight (1801) made similar experiments using dyes and ringing technics. He noted that decreased foliage resulted in decreased growth between the foliage and the root. He concluded that sap, rising in the vessels of the wood, is carried into leaves where, in the presence of air and light, it acquires organic matter and is subsequently conveyed to all parts of the plant, providing nourishment for growth.

Dutrochet (1827) introduced the concept of endosmosis as a force in bringing about sap movement; de Candolle (1832) proposed that a special organ at the root tip (contractile spongiole) served to bring about water uptake from the soil.

The first half of the nineteenth century witnessed great activity in investigations on the anatomy of plants and simultaneously the birth of a true spirit of objective scientific investigation. The description of the sieve tube by Hartig in 1837 made possible a real basis for differentiation between phloem and xylem transport. Hartig also observed phloem exudation and he proposed that downward movement of organic solutes takes place in the phloem.

With the recognition of the distinct nature of the two basic conducting tissues of plants, and the accumulating evidence for the immense amounts of water that are commonly lost from plants by transpiration, emphasis shifted to a search for the mechanism responsible for the upward movement of the transpiration stream. Whereas Dutrochet had advanced the idea that endosmosis might be involved in the uptake of water, von Mohl (1851) pointed out that the osmotically active substances of the wood are contained in the living cells of parenchyma and rays and not in the tracheids and vessels. He had no explanation for the entry of sap into these xylem conduits.

Sachs, in 1874, recognizing the difficulties in explaining sap movement in xylem elements, proposed that water moves in an imbibed state in the tracheal walls and that living cells play no direct role while the lumina of the elongated xylem cells are filled with air bubbles during the time of most active movement (Sachs, 1882).

By filling the lumina of xylem conduits with cacao butter and making a fresh transverse cut, Vesque (1884) and Elfving (1882) presented evidence that refuted Sachs' imbibition theory, for the leaves of branches treated in this way rapidly wilted and did not recover. Errera (1886) and Strasburger (1891) confirmed these experiments using gelatin, and Dixon (1914) did the same with paraffin and ice.

Meanwhile Boehm (1863) and Hartig (1882) proposed that gas pressure was responsible for movement of the xylem stream. These men, along with Sachs and many others, were impressed with the great number of air bubbles that normally occur in cut branches when the bark is stripped off and the woody tissues are examined under the microscope. In fact, so impressed was E. B. Copeland (1902) with the occurrence of intermittent columns of air and water in the xylem that he proposed the idea that the nature of the Jamin's chains was such as to promote the rise of sap to the top of tall trees.

With the abandonment of the imbibition theory the pendulum swung to the opposite pole in the ideas of Godlewski (1884) who postulated a pumping action of living cells to explain the rise of xylem sap. In this scheme the wood ray cells act as pumps whereas the tracheae serve as conduits. Air pressure was viewed as resisting downward flow and assisting in a stepwise pumping action. Janse (1887, 1913) and Westermaier (1883) supported in different ways this same vital theory of sap movement and throughout the latter part of the nineteenth century controversy raged between the proponents of the "vital" and the "physical" theories.

Oddly enough, Boucherie (1840) had shown many years earlier that a woody stem placed in a poisonous liquid would draw the liquid up to its highest leaves and continue to take it up even after the leaves were dead. It remained, however, for Strasburger (1891) to prove conclusively the purely physical nature of sap movement in the xylem. By heat treatment, dyes, and poisons he proved that water would move through dead stems and rise to the top of dead woody shoots. His exhaustive studies certainly leave little to be desired as far as proof for the futility of the vital theories is concerned.

It was Dixon and Joly (1894) who evaluated a truly satisfactory theory to explain the rise of sap in tall plants. In their "Cohesion theory" they described a mechanism that has stood the test of detailed examination for over 50 years. They showed, in purely physical apparatus, that water and extracted xylem sap will persist in a tensile state, due to cohesion of the water molecules and adhesion of water to glass.

Askenasy (1896) soon showed that tension in a moving water column may be readily demonstrated in physical apparatus, and by a very ingenious method Ursprung (1915) proved that water in the dead annulus cells of a fern sporangium will withstand tension up to 300 atmospheres. Bode (1923) has described experiments with living plants that prove the existence of tensile water columns in living wood and Crafts (1939b) has confirmed his observations. More recent work by Greenidge (1954, 1955a, b) has proved the continuous nature of the aqueous phase in plants and the fact that the water continuum may surmount rather serious barriers and still maintain an adequate supply for normal transpiration. Scholander and associates (1955, 1957) have proved that vapor bubbles in the vine do not prevent the movement of the transpiration stream.

Thus, starting with a wholly erroneous picture, plant physiologists by a tedious process of experimentation lasting over 300 years have finally arrived at a satisfying view of the mechanism of sap movement in the xylem. Similar in many ways is the history of discovery in the field of phloem transport.

MOVEMENT OF ASSIMILATES

With the description of the sieve tube by Hartig (1837, 1854) and the study of phloem exudation (1858a, b), ground was laid for a true distinction between the two major vascular systems of the plant and an assignment of each to its proper role in the overall processes of growth and metabolism. Hartig proposed that downward transfer of organic assimilates takes place in the phloem and he recognized the part that protoplasmic streaming might play in their distribution.

By ringing plants having collateral, bicollateral, and scattered bundles Hanstein (1860) arrived at the conclusion that the sieve tubes alone conduct organic materials from leaves to points of utilization and he pointed out the relation of the phloem to the nutrition of the cambium.

Nageli (1861) studied the phloem tissues of cucurbits and decided that only the less diffusible nitrogenous compounds are transported in them. He found that the sap that exudes from cucurbit stems comes only from phloem tissues and he supposed that the movement of sap in the sieve tubes was caused by changing turgidity in the surrounding cells. Sachs (1863) differentiated between carbohydrates and nitrogenous compounds as to their channels of movement. He held that while the latter move through the sieve tubes in the manner described by Nageli, carbohydrates are confined to the parenchyma tissues that surround the phloem and they move by diffusion alone.

De Vries (1885), realizing that diffusion was too slow to account for the rapid conduction of carbohydrates to storage tissues, suggested that protoplasmic movements offered the best explanation. He made observations on tissues of many species and found streaming and rotation a common phenomenon, especially in the phloem. By careful ringing experiments Heine (1885) was able to show that the starch-bearing parenchymatous layer that surrounds the phloem in many stems, and termed by Sachs the starch sheath, does not act as conducting tissue for carbohydrates. He thought that it served to store starch to be used later in the thickening of the bast-fiber walls.

By microchemical and macrochemical analysis Zacharias (1884) showed that the sap exuded from the phloem of cucurbit stems contained proteins of the fibrin group, organic nitrogen compounds that showed reducing properties upon hydrolysis, and, in the ash, potash, phosphoric acid, and magnesium. Gregor Kraus (1885) analyzed the exuded sap from cucurbit fruits and found that it contained from 7 to 11 percent dry matter. Of this about 15 percent was protein, from 9 to 64 percent was sugar, and about 5 percent was phosphoric acid. Potassium was the predominating basic element and Kraus confirmed the statement of Zacharias that it accounted for the alkaline reaction of the sap.

Fisher (1885) studying the anatomy of sieve tubes in the Cucurbitaceae found that by killing and fixing with hot water he could demonstrate a lack of the slime plugs shown in the older drawings. He concluded that this accumulation at the sieve plate is an artifact resulting from cutting the stem while the sieve tube contents are in a fluid condition and that it is caused by a filtering of the protein particles from the moving sap.

The movement of carbohydrates out of leaves was being widely studied when Schimper (1885) published his paper. The work is typified by his experiments with cleared leaves treated with iodine. By microscopic examination of this material he came to the conclusion that transfer was along the veins and that the material moved by diffusion in the form of glucose and moved as if through open conduits rather than through a system of closed cells. He thought that the conducting parenchyma of the vascular strands constituted the principal channels.

Strasburger (1891) described the vascular anatomy of many species. He found the sieve plates of gymnosperms to be closed whereas those of many angiosperms he considered to be traversed by small pores. He noted the presence of exudation pressures in the phloem tissues of both gymnosperms and angiosperms, but although the sap of the former was watery that from the latter contained slime and protoplasm. His conclusion was that the swelled closing membrane of the sieve plate offers no more resistance to the movement of a watery solution than does the closing membrane of the bordered pit in wood. He pictured the movement of nitrogenous materials as taking place through the sieve tubes from the point of synthesis to that of utilization, lateral distribution being effected by diffusion through the rays. Phloem parenchyma he considered as serving to conduct carbohydrates, store proteins and carbohydrates, and eliminate by-products of metabolism. Czapek (1897) thought, on the other hand, that transfer of all organic materials takes place through the sieve tubes, the remaining cells of the phloem serving chiefly as storage tissue. In his experiments he ringed stems, cut away halves of petioles, and used heat, chloroform, and plasmolyzing agents on petioles. He thought that diffusion was too slow to account for the movement of organic nutrients and that changes in turgor, protoplasmic movements, and the condensations of assimilation were not effective. Rather, he concluded that the living protoplasm has some vital ability to take up materials from one place and pass them on, this process continuing throughout the channels of movement.

Improved histological technique was responsible for increasing accuracy in the study of phloem anatomy during the latter part of the nineteenth century. The two publications of A. W. Hill (1901, 1908) give clear descriptions of sieve-tube development of gymnosperms and angiosperms.

Ewart (1903) wrote a monograph on protoplasmic streaming and calculated the energy requirements from physical laws. He considered the part played in the transfer of solutes to be entirely secondary, the number and variety of agents that may stimulate or retard streaming seeming to preclude the possibility of a direct relationship. He did suggest, however, that streaming through sieve pores might effect a direct transfer of the watery contents of the tubes. From a study of the factors affecting protoplasmic movements in several aquatic plants Bierburg (1908) concluded that the rate of movement of solutes in transport might be accelerated three to four times by streaming but that only in plants lacking a well-differentiated vascular system did this take place.

Deleano (1911) found that by cutting, scalding, or chloroforming the vascular bundles of the petiole he could hinder the loss of starch from the grape leaf. Scalding depressed the rate to one-third its original value and chloroforming to one-half. Ruhland (1912) studied the permeability of leaf cells and vascular tissues of *Beta vulgaris* for cane and invert sugars by the plasmolytic method. He found sieve tubes to be no more permeable to these sugars than the phloem parenchyma and could not agree with Czapek as to their role in sugar transport. He found phloem cells of the root to be even less permeable than those of leaf veins.

Haberlandt (1914) assigned functions to the different phloem elements based upon their form. He thought that the elongated parenchyma cells serve principally in conduction of carbohydrates whereas sieve tubes transport proteinaceous materials.

Mangham (1917) extended Czapek's view and attempted to give a physicochemical explanation for the mechanism suggested by the latter. He pictured the conduction of sugar as taking place entirely within the mass of the protoplasm without passing through the plasmatic membrane and considered the sieve tube as the chief element concerned in longitudinal transfer. Kidd (1918) criticized the physicochemical concepts upon which Mangham based his hypothesis, finding no justification for the assumption that movement would take place against a diffusion gradient or at a rate greater than that of natural diffusion.

Schmidt (1917) considered that sieve tubes are normal living cells during their period of activity. He claimed they contained cytoplasm, nuclei, and chromatophores, and could not be assigned a special function on the basis of structure. He concluded that nothing definite is known concerning the function of sieve tubes but that apparently the whole phloem system serves to transport organic materials. Following a series of ringing experiments upon woody plants, Curtis (1920a) concluded that longitudinal transfer of sugars takes place principally through the phloem. He pointed out (1920b) the part played by developing leaves in the supply of organic nutrients to newly growing shoots and was of the opinion that normally there is no upward movement of food from the roots and none from the main trunk.

Birch-Hirschfeld (1919) found diffusion too slow to account for the movement of plastic materials. Protoplasmic streaming did not accelerate transport in her experiments and she does not agree with De Vries' hypothesis but suggests backward movement through the xylem as an alternative. The small size of phloem elements and the viscid nature of their contents appeared to Dixon (1923) and to Dixon and Ball (1922) as insurmountable obstacles to the conduction of organic nutrients by this tissue. They elaborated further the mechanism suggested by Birch-Hirschfeld, giving experimental data and calculating rates of movement. In a later publication (1923) these authors suggested that the phloem may be more properly considered as storage and secretory tissue. Mason (1923) recorded that although ringing reduced the weight of storage roots of the Bitter Cassava to about one-fourth that of the roots of unringed plants, the tops were somewhat larger than normal. In view of Dixon's theory Mason suggested that the phloem may act in transmission of carbohydrates but does not provide the actual conduits.

Unable to meet the criticisms of Dixon and Ball and Birch-Hirschfeld, Kastens (1924) tried to explain the results of her ringing experiments on the assumption that the phloem conducts hormones that affect the growth and metabolism of plants. Following additional experiments in which the effects of ringing and removal of xylem were compared, Curtis (1925) concluded that solutes moved both upward and downward through the phloem and that this movement is accelerated by protoplasmic streaming. Mason and Lewin (1926), on the other hand, found an exceedingly high rate of transport necessary to deliver the calculated amounts of carbohydrates through the observed cross section of sieve tubes and concluded, therefore, that normal transfer must take place through the xylem.

Of special significance is a paper published by Ernst Münch (1927). He described a physical system in which a maintained concentration gradient between two osmotic cells causes a mass flow of solution from the higher to the lower concentration through a connecting tube, water exchange taking place through the semipermeable walls of the cells. He applied this system to the plant, assuming that photosynthesis maintains the concentration difference between assimilating cells and storage or meristematic tissues, the sieve tubes acting as the connecting elements. Experiments were described in which exudation from the cambium and excessive growth resulted from interruption of the descending sap. Cutting the phloem caused a very rapid decrease in exudation pressure, especially below the cut; this decrease was transmitted downward at a rate of 10 centimeters per second for as far as 6 meters. Münch calculated the rate of flow necessary to account for certain known increases in dry weight of trees and estimated that about 2½ percent of the total water used by the tree circulates through the phloem system. He suggested that transfer of assimilate from leaf parenchyma to sieve tubes takes place along the plasmodesmata, assuming, as did Mangham, that the property of selective permeability is confined to the outer layer of the protoplast.

The most convincing of the ringing experiments are those conducted on cotton plants by Mason and Maskel (1928a, 1928b). By carefully controlled work they produced evidence for the downward movement of sugar through the bark along a concentration gradient. This conclusion was based on results showing that diurnal changes in the sugar content of leaves were reproduced a few hours later in the bark, but not in the wood; carbohydrate content of the sap in leaf, bark, and wood increased rapidly above a ring and decreased below; removal of bark stopped transport whereas separation of bark and wood did not; and transport took place into loosened flaps of bark. They suggested that longitudinal movement of sugar occurs in the sieve tubes, that it follows a diffusion pattern, and that the rate is about 40,000 times that of diffusion from a 2 percent solution of sucrose. While concluding that "transport occurs through stationary cytoplasm" (Mason and Phillis, 1937) by a process they term "activated diffusion," they admit that the data upon which they base the analogy with physical diffusion do not exclude an explanation by the pressure-flow hypothesis of Münch (Mason and Phillis, 1937). In a review of these papers Priestley (1929a) pointed out the part that young developing sieve tubes might play in this transfer owing to the active streaming that occurs in them. He also suggested that the condensation of hexoses to sucrose may accompany the differentiation of the sieve tubes.

In a series of memorable papers Maskell and Mason (1929a, b; 1930a, b, c) attacked the problem of nitrogen movement in the cotton plant. They conclude that for nitrogen as well as for carbohydrate transport there appears to be a gradient basis. For carbohydrates the source seems to supply reducing sugars that are transformed to sucrose in the sieve tubes. For nitrogen they conclude the labile form to be residual N. Within the sieve tubes, all soluble carbohydrates and labile forms of nitrogen including protein they picture as contributing to longitudinal transport, the part of each depending on the gradient maintained. The mechanism, they think, should act impartially on all materials that are free to move.

It seems unfortunate that Maskell and Mason started this work and interpreted their results on the belief that "the bulk of the mineral nitrogen absorbed by the roots is carried in the transpiration current to the leaves, where it is elaborated to amino acids etc., and then exported through the sieve tubes back to the roots etc." As a result of this assumption they find the gradients of total sugars and of organic crystalloid N to be in opposite directions. To rationalize this with the above belief they conclude that there exists in the bark of cotton a dynamic gradient of mobile N masked by a static gradient of storage N; and the mobile fraction they say is residual N whereas the static fraction consists of protein N and crystalloidal N.

The data of Maskell and Mason are not in conflict with the pressure-flow concept of phloem conduction if one examines the results of their nitrogen work with the view that the soil is the source and the whole plant the sink of N, that reduction of inorganic N to organic forms can occur in roots (Thomas, 1927; Pierre and Pohlman, 1933) and that these reduced N compounds may move up with the transpiration stream, and, finally, that excess N not required by leaves may be moved with sugars in the phloem to regions of growth.

By chilling the petioles of bean leaves and by surrounding them with an atmosphere of nitrogen Curtis (1929) hindered removal of carbohydrates from the leaves and concluded that translocation through the phloem is dependent upon the activity of living cells.

Impressed with the suggestions of Ruhland (1912) that sieve tubes could be plasmolyzed and with E. W. Schmidt's conclusion that specialization of the sieve tube did not fit it to the function of rapid conduction of organic foods, Crafts (1931) proposed that translocation of foods in the plant may take place via the total phloem with the bulk of the movement occurring in the walls. This is an elaboration of an earlier suggestion of Priestley (1929b) that movement of foods from differentiating protophloem sieve tubes to the apical meristems might take place along the cell walls.

Schumacher (1930) described a technic for closing the sieve pores of *Pelargonium* phloem by means of dilute eosin solution without visible injury to phloem parenchyma. Since such closing of the sieve plates prevented export of both carbohydrates and nitrogenous compounds from leaves, Schumacher produced positive evidence that the sieve tubes constitute the channels of transport of the phloem.

Later Schumacher (1933) reported that fluorescein, applied to leaves in droplets of gelatin, entered the sieve tubes and moved in the parietal cytoplasm. He claimed that fluorescein was not present in the lumen and that its movement in the cytoplasm was not caused by protoplasmic streaming. Schumacher found the pores of sieve plates to be filled with cytoplasm and fluorescein could be seen to traverse these in stems of cucurbits.

Van den Honert (1932) proposed a mechanism for rapid interfacial movement along a diffusion gradient to explain phloem transport. Because he suggested the vacuole-cytoplasm interface as the possible site of such movement his idea has been criticized by Mason and Phillis (1937) and Crafts (1936). After detailed studies on the phloem anatomy of cucurbits (1932) and potato (1933) Crafts abandoned his idea of phloem conduction via the cell walls. He found that when he cut thick sections of the stems of these plants into buffered neutral red and carried out plasmolysis tests, mature sieve-tube elements failed to plasmolyze whereas young sieve tubes and all phloem parenchyma cells showed definite plasmolysis. He concluded that the protoplasts of sieve tubes became completely permeable at maturity and that the bulk of the mass flow takes place through the lumina, the principal resistance being in the sieve plates. Huber and Rouschal (1938) agreed with this interpretation.

Huber and his associates, working on forest trees, have contributed much to our understanding of phloem function. Huber (1937) reported studies on phloem exudate from trees. Using a hand refractometer, he studied the diurnal cycle of concentration differences. Huber, Schmidt, and Jahnel (1937) made extended studies on the phloem exudate from several tree species. Accepting Wislicenus' (1933) analyses, indicating that in phloem exudate from trees the dry weight consists of sucrose to the extent of 80 percent (see also Moose, 1938), they determined the refractive index, which they reported simply as an arbitrary concentration. Their values varied from around 16 percent to as high as 27 percent with an average of about 20 percent. The daily variations were within 2 to 3 percent, the low values found in the morning and the high values in the afternoon. There was a concentration gradient from the crown to the base of the trunk. Pfieffer (1937) had also found this.

Finding daily fluctuations in concentration, Huber, Schmidt, and Jahnel undertook a detailed study of concentration changes with time at three heights on large red oak trees having 50 feet or more of clear trunk. In July 1937 they measured concentration changes at 10, 6, and 2 meters throughout a three-day period. They found significant evidence for a daily time reduction in concentration from the top downward, followed later by a rise. In August they found the same changes. Considering the daily concentration minima, the changes with time indicated a downward flow of phloem sap at 2 meters per hour in July, and at 3.6 meters per hour in August. The writers point out that these fluctuations did not correspond with shifts in water balance, but that the volume of sap did reflect the water status in that it was greatest during mornings and evenings and lowest at midday. That some adjustment to water balance was involved was shown by the higher concentration at the top of the trunk and by observation that daily fluctuations of 2 to 3 percent occurred at 10 to 12.5 meters and only 1 percent at 2 meters.

Huber and Rouschal (1938) have reported detailed studies on the properties of sieve-tube cytoplasm. They found the sieve tubes of most trees to be active only during one season and they proposed that the cytoplasm of the functioning elements is in a "premortal" state characterized by a highly permeable condition. Plasmolysis and vital staining succeeded only in young sieve tubes; the cytoplasm of mature elements they considered to die during preparation of sections, although *Cucurbita* seemed to be an exception. They unsuccessfully attempted to introduce vital dyes into vacuoles of cucurbit sieve tubes. They pointed to the modified permeability of the sieve-tube cytoplasm as an example of specialization in the phloem comparable with the complete loss of protoplasm by xylem elements.

In a fourth paper, Huber (1939) gave a detailed description and analysis of the structure and function of sieve tubes of trees. He concluded that in the majority of trees, a single band of sieve tubes develops each year, attaining its greatest width in September and collapsing after leaf fall. Narrow sieve tubes formed during late autumn may survive the winter, especially in trees having ring porous wood. In some trees several bands are formed separated by fiber bands; these also function only one season. *Tilia* apparently develops sieve tubes that function two or more years. The narrowness (usually around ¼ mm) of the annual sieve-tube increment in many trees is compensated by the high concentration of the assimilate stream so that the amount of material carried by the phloem is about the same as that transported in the xylem. Phloem development is reduced from the crown down the trunk but the reduction is not as great as that in the quantity of assimilates carried.

Meanwhile, Leonard (1938) demonstrated polar movement of sugar from the blade to the petiole in excised sugar beet leaves. He showed (1939) that sugars from mature beet leaves placed in the dark moved into the petioles until the blades were depleted. This occurred both in detached leaves and in leaves growing on plants. Since there was no tendency for accumulation at the base of the petiole, Leonard concluded that the polar movement was brought about by the border parenchyma of the blades, being a function of tissues at the source rather than at the sink.

Leonard found no reversal of translocation into bagged mature leaves and concluded that mature mesophyll is unable to absorb sugars actively from the phloem. In contrast to mature leaves, young growing leaves readily utilized sugars moved up from the roots. Leonard proposed that the mechanism of polarized movement is not developed until late in the growth of the leaf. Blades of etiolated leaves imported sugar from the petioles. Sucrose gradients in the petioles of these etiolated leaves indicate a diffusion from the petiole and an accumulation in the blade—a reversal of the normal polar movement.

Engard (1939a), studying carbohydrate metabolism in raspberry, concluded that sucrose is the principal sugar translocated in the phloem. Transport occurs from roots into growing shoots in spring, later from leaves downward. When a segment of stem is isolated by two rings, an accumulation occurs above and below the isolated part, and sucrose entirely disappears between the rings.

Reporting on transport of nitrogenous substances in raspberry, Engard (1939b) found that nitrate is the principal translocated form of nitrogen, movement taking place in the xylem. Although there are positive gradients of nitrogenous substances in the stem, these do not indicate downward movement because there is no accumulation of nitrogen in the bark above a ring and the gradient is not reversed or even leveled during the season. Upward movement of organic nitrogen in the bark is not important because there is no accumulation below the lower ring and the nitrogen above the rings remains normal by continued supply through the xylem. In contrast to Maskell and Mason, Engard stated that elaboration of nitrates to amino acids and protein is not restricted to leaves alone but occurs in all living cells where the proper conditions for nitrate reduction exist.

Schumacher (1939) reported studies on the plasmolyzability of sieve tubes, describing results of work on 27 different plants. Using petioles and veins of *Pelargonium,* he found that fully developed elements capable of conduction of fluorescein could be plasmolyzed. Sucrose was better than KNO_3, $Ca(NO_3)_2$, or glycerin.

Attempting to test the mass-flow mechanism, Clements (1940) measured the growth of fruits of the sausage tree, *Kigelia africana.* From weekly measurements he calculated weekly dry weight increases of fruits and converted these to hexose sugar equivalents. He determined total and reducing sugars in the phloem and the dry weight and cross-sectional area. Assuming that all of the water in the phloem is mobile, Clements calculated that 5.7 liters of the 0.62 percent sugar solution would have to traverse the phloem of the peduncle daily to account for the growth of the fruits. Since this daily volume increment could not remain in the fruit, Clements calculated that 5.4 liters of water would have to move back through the xylem daily. Upon slitting the bark and freeing the cut xylem cylinder, Clements found no exudation of water and so concluded that the mass-flow mechanism was inadequate.

Had Clements been able to measure the dry weight composition of the assimilate stream he very probably would have found it to be in the range of 6 to 20 percent. The fruit of the sausage tree, if it resembles fruits of cucurbits, might have a dry weight composition considerably below this value (Crafts 1932, Table VII). The total volume of the phloem sap would be consumed under these conditions and additional water from the xylem would be required. This is probably the condition wherever the principal function of the assimilate stream is to provide nutrients for growth.

Because Clements found the greatest growth increments of his fruits during the first five weeks of development, he assumed that the sieve tubes leading into the fruits were immature and hence in a high state of metabolic activity. Had he been familiar with phloem ontogeny he would have realized that even in the bud stage there were mature protophloem sieve tubes in the peduncle; in the flower there were probably mature metaphloem sieve tubes; and in the fruit there was undoubtedly much primary and possibly even secondary phloem.

Cooil (1941), using squash plants in three metabolic categories, attempted to determine how truly phloem exudate represents sieve-tube contents, what forces cause exudation, and how the mechanism of phloem export functions. He found that the flow of exudate was greatest from the petioles of the minus-nitrate plants and least from the low-carbohydrate plants. This was in inverse relation to the sugar concentration of the exudate, and directly correlated with the sugar concentration of the tissues. Since the exudation was greatest in the plants where translocation was reduced, and least in the vegetative plants where growth demanded the greatest transport of assimilates, Cooil concluded that no relation exists between exudation and translocation. When it is recalled that exudate was collected for only one minute from each cut, it seems reasonable to conclude that pressure in the phloem was greatest in the minus-nitrate plants where carbohydrates were piled up because growth was lacking. In the young actively growing plants, growth was creating a sink where assimilates were being used up, and hence in these plants phloem pressure would be low. Concerning the relation of sugar concentration to phloem exudation, the mass-flow mechanism requires only that the assimilates in transport be osmotically active. The total dry weight of the phloem exudate is a closer approach to the osmotic activity of solute than is sugar concentration. Cooil found dry weight contents as high as 9 percent and he considered that much of this was protein. Though nitrogenous in nature, it probably had simpler molecular structure (Crafts, 1954) and hence higher osmotic activity.

Because of the high nitrogen content of the phloem exudate, Cooil assumed that the protein was high, hence the sieve tubes were highly active. Since it had been amply proved that the phloem exudate of squash proceeds from long distances through uncut cells (Crafts, 1936) before it flows from the cut surface, it seems difficult to visualize leakage of proteinaceous contents from such active cells. Studies on absorption and loss of mineral elements from living cells indicate a low activity state when loss is great, and many reports on phloem anatomy assume a low activity for mature functioning sieve tubes (Crafts, 1939c; Esau, 1939, 1950).

Rouschal (1941) reported on sieve-tube studies, interpreting changes in the protoplast with maturation as resulting in a highly sensitive state. He noted the loss of lipids and tannins by the maturing elements, the increase in hydration, and the extreme lability of the elements upon cutting. By bathing the tissues with a concentrated glycerin solution, he was able to relax the pressure so that little exudation occurred. When exposed to a plasmolyzing solution, tissues so treated responded by plasmolysis of the sieve tubes. When treated with calcium and aluminum salts the sieve-tube cytoplasm was hardened. Rouschal interpreted his plasmolysis tests as indicating that the side-wall protoplasm of the sieve tubes is semipermeable, the end-wall protoplasm highly permeable.

Huber (1941) reviewed the subject of assimilate movement and discussed the plasmolyzability of sieve tubes. He described work by Leonhardt (1940) on honeydew production by aphids. Using a single insect under controlled conditions, Leonhardt counted the number of droplets for 24 hours. He found a diurnal fluctuation in honeydew production that paralleled assimilation values in studies on photosynthesis, and in sieve-tube sap concentrations found by Huber, Schmidt, and Jahnel (1937). Huber expressed the conviction that osmotic gradients actually occur in sieve tubes and that sieve tubes are permeable to the constituents of the exudate.

In laying a background for a review of the sieve tubes as a source of nutrients for foreign organisms and as conduits for virus movement, Huber (1942) listed a series of sieve-tube properties that have been determined with some certainty. He mentioned the very narrow layer of active sieve tubes in the bark of trees, the basally directed pressure gradient in the active sieve tubes, the daily fluctuation in pressure corresponding to the diurnal cycle of light and dark, the late appearance of phloem exudation in forest trees (late summer), the demonstration of phloem exudation from conifers by use of the "Schlierenmethode," and the prolonged sap flow from cucurbits with repeated cutting.

Colwell (1942a) studied phloem exudation and fruit and exudate composition of pumpkin. Table 2-1 gives some of his data.

Table 2-1

Size and Composition of Pumpkin Fruits; Composition of Phloem Exudate

Size of fruits (in grams)	Dry weight (in percent)		Total carbon (in percent)		Total nitrogen	
	fruit	exudate	fruit	exudate	fruit	exudate
40	7.0	8.3	3.00	3.03	0.40	0.81
450	5.7	9.3	2.43	2.94	0.18	0.78
1600	5.7	10.8	2.40	4.04	0.13	0.97
6000	6.3	11.7	2.66	4.44	0.18	1.00
10000	8.1	13.7	3.28	2.98	0.24	0.68

The dry weight of the exudate was consistently higher than that of the fruits.

Of the total carbon of the exudate, roughly $9/10$ is associated with nitrogen compounds and $1/10$ with sugars. Phloem exudate contained only 4.3 times as much carbon as nitrogen; the fruit has 13.7 times as much carbon as nitrogen.

Colwell found that the sieve-tube sap of pumpkin is diluted about 10 percent in the first minute after cutting a stem and that it gradually assumes a constant value. Using sections of the peduncles of fruits for measuring phloem areas, and taking growth increment measures on pumpkin, Colwell calculated that average rates of linear flow of the assimilate stream of 200 cm per hour through the sieve tubes would be required to account for the observed rates of growth.

Crafts and Lorenz (1944a, b) continued studies on fruit growth and phloem exudate from cucurbits. They found, as did Colwell, that the C/N ratio of the fruit is from 3 to 6 times as great as that of the exudate. Concluding that this rules out the use of phloem exudate of cucurbits as a true sample of sieve-tube sap, they pointed out that growth of cucurbit fruits may still serve as an index of the rate of normal food movement. Using 39 Connecticut Field pumpkin fruits for measurements and recording growth from August 5 to September 7, they calculated that dry assimilate would have to move on the average of 11.0 cm per hour to account for growth; a 10 percent solution would move about 110 cm per hour. Similar measurements on Early Prolific Straightneck summer squash gave a value of 13.4 cm per hour between September 7 and 18; this corresponds with 134 cm per hour for a 10 percent solution of assimilates. These values must be multiplied by a factor of 2 to 5 to arrive at flow rate through the protoplasmic strands of the sieve plates.

Went (1944) found translocation in the tomato plant to be low at 26.5° C but appreciable at 18° C, as indicated by accumulation of sucrose above a steamed ring on the stem. In experiments on bleeding from excised tomato root systems, rates were inversely correlated with temperature. Analyzing these responses, Went concluded that translocation of sugar occurs principally at night, increasing as the night temperature decreases to 8° C. Went concluded further that above 18° C sugar translocation limits growth of stems as well as of roots and fruits of tomato. Below 18° C the growth process itself becomes limiting. Further work (Went, 1945) appeared to confirm these conclusions.

In extensive studies on carbohydrate metabolism in sugar beet, Willam (1945) found that reducing sugars produced in the mesophyll of beet leaves are translocated toward the phloem of the leaf veins. In the veins these are condensed to sucrose, which in turn is translocated down the petiole into the root where it is accumulated. Sugar beet research workers know that the overall transport of sugar in the sugar beet is polarized; that is, it runs from low sucrose concentrations in the mesophyll to higher concentrations in petioles and even higher in roots. If the concentration process occurs in the border parenchyma of vein endings in the leaf and in phloem parenchyma of vascular bundles, and if absorption from sieve tubes and storage in parenchyma of roots is active, movement within the sieve tubes may still proceed along a gradient.

Loomis (1945), reporting translocation studies on maize, found that sucrose is exchanged between the phloem and the pith of the stem but he questioned the ability of the lignified cells of the bundle sheath to transport sugar. It has commonly been observed, however, that lignified fibers of grape store starch and hence are living; if the bundle-sheath cells of maize are living they therefore should transport sugar readily.

Loomis concludes that sucrose is the sugar commonly translocated in maize. Believing that neither the activated diffusion nor the pressure-flow mechanism will explain the polarized type of movement found in maize, he suggests that new hypotheses are needed. He presents data proving that sugars are moved from leaves containing 0.3 percent sucrose through tissues containing 7 or 8 percent sucrose. Leonard's work (1938, 1939) on polar movement in sugar beet is cited, as are the results of Phillis and Mason (1933) on cotton as further evidence for polar movement. Loomis provides convincing evidence on the effect of pollinated maize ears on the movement of sugar from leaves and basal branches into these active sinks.

Few question the evidence for polar movement reported by Loomis and Leonard. The crux of the problem is the location of the polar mechanism. If, as Phillis and Mason propose, the border parenchyma cells are able to concentrate sugars in the phloem of the veins, and if, as Crafts suggested in 1931 and 1932, storage parenchyma cells or meristematic tissues can accumulate sugars actively and so lower concentration in the phloem, it seems possible that either of the above-named mechanisms may operate in the sieve tubes proper. It should be emphasized that neither the activated-diffusion nor the pressure-flow hypothesis was suggested to explain polar movement over short distances. They were proposed to account for the rapid transport of assimilates from points of synthesis to points of utilization, often over meters. Until such time as both hypotheses may be proved untenable, the problem is to develop a picture of an integrated mechanism utilizing any concepts that fit the known structural and physiological properties of the phloem.

Went and Engelsburg (1946), studying the sucrose content of leaves, stems, and roots of tomato held at 8°, 17°, and 26° C for 12 hours in the dark, found sucrose in the leaves and roots to be higher in the 8° plants than in the 17° plants. Between 17° and 26° the roots had less sugar at the higher temperature, the leaves slightly more. They concluded that translocation is less at the higher temperature.

Hewitt and Curtis (1948), using bean, tomato, and milkweed plants, determined respirational and translocational losses of dry weight and carbohydrate from matched leaves of plants held at 4°, 10°, 20°, 30°, and 40° C for 13 hours in the dark. In all experiments, respirational losses ran from around 10 mg per gram dry weight at 4° C to around 100 mg at 40° C. Translocational losses starting around the same magnitude were doubled at 10° C and trebled between 10° and 20° C. At 30° the losses equaled those at 20°, and at 40° they were significantly less. This decrease was interpreted as being due to depletion of carbohydrate reserves in the 13-hour period at 40° by respiration. Carbohydrate results approximated those for dry weight, and experiments with tomato, milkweed, and corn did not differ.

On the basis of these results Hewitt and Curtis criticize the interpretation of Went and of Went and Engelsburg that translocation decreases as temperature is raised. They contend that respiration at the higher temperatures is speeded so that reserves are expended, hence transport at the source is lessened.

Crafts (1948) attempted to describe a structure of the sieve-tube walls and cytoplasm that might enable these elements to conduct the rapid flow of solution evidenced by phloem exudation and visualized by advocates of the pressure-flow hypothesis. He proposed that degradation of the cytoplasm results in openings of the order of 125 to 350 Å. Maturation of the sieve-tube cytoplasm is pictured as accompanied by loss of lipid and polar groups along the protein chains, leaving a screenlike skeleton. This would agree with Rouschal's (1941) conclusions. Thermal agitation should jostle the molecules and keep the channels of transport open.

Arens (1948) proposed an "active-membrane" hypothesis to explain many polar movements in plants. Factors changing the work of the active membrane could transform a concentrically polarized (accumulating) cell into a laterally polarized (translocating) one. Thus an oxygen gradient might bring about polarized movement into sieve tubes, and a gradient of potassium ions—augmenting the dispersion of proteins in the pores—might explain the difference in permeability between side-wall and end-wall protoplasm of sieve tubes postulated by Rouschal (1941).

Roeckl (1949) concluded that the cells involved in assimilation have significantly lower osmotic values than has the sieve-tube sap. The concentration increases stepwise from tissue to tissue from palisade through spongy and border parenchyma to sieve tubes. Movements, therefore, cannot be a simple hydraulic pressure flow in Münch's sense but must involve an active process. From the many evidences of polar movement it seems increasingly certain that active accumulation, or possibly secretion, is involved in the first stage of assimilate transport. It may be equally true that active accumulation of assimilate from sieve tubes constitutes the last stage.

Went and Hull (1949) reported further work indicating a negative temperature coefficient for translocation in tomato. A disturbing feature of their work is the fact that the plants with chilled stems had no more sugar in their roots than the unchilled plants. From their work, which involved feeding sugar to leaves and measuring bleeding from cut stems under different temperature treatments, it seems as logical to conclude that the $O_2:CO_2$ relation of the roots is affected so that the cooling brings more rapid bleeding.

Hull reported the inhibition of transport by high temperatures again (1952), using C^{14}-labeled glucose and sucrose. On the other hand, Swanson and Böhning (1951), Böhning *et al.* (1952), Böhning *et al.* (1953), Swanson and Whitney (1953), Vernon and Aronoff (1952), and Kendall (1952) all agree that translocation is retarded by low temperature and accelerated by high temperature. Bauer (1953) found that lowering of temperature reduced the dry weight of adventitious roots of sunflower seedlings.

In two review articles Kursanov (1956a, 1956b) describes work in Russia on translocation. Kursanov discards diffusion as a mechanism to accelerate movement; he also questions the mechanisms of Münch, Mason and his associates, Dixon, Schumacher, Curtis, and Rouschal. Failing to find a concentration gradient in the phloem, Kursanov proposes that movement occurs as "an active transfer of the molecules themselves due to a peculiar biochemical activity of the conducting cells." He says "We are still far from understanding those complicated phenomena resulting in the transformation of energy of biochemical reactions into a form of energy which drives diverse organic substances rapidly in one direction or another." Since translocation of sugars "is as a rule accompanied by an almost complete invariability of the total sugar content," the "sieve cells do not possess any reserve capacity to let through a wave of moving substances, and the act of translocation is based rather on the principle of push whereby the substance starts moving throughout the length of the moving path."

This mechanism is reminiscent of that described by Schumacher (1937) for fluorescein. Kursanov describes phloem as having extremely high rates of respiration, particularly when sucrose is in transport. Kursanov (1956a) suggests that there is a close connection between the act of translocation and the functioning of the cytochrome system. He states that translocation of substances in conducting cells is accompanied by their transformation and that the conducting tissues of plants are capable of oxidation-reduction reactions and many reactions of carbohydrate-phosphorus metabolism. This, he states, ensures the mobilization of energy required for the transfer of molecules while the inert sugar molecules are converted into mobile ions by coupling either with phosphoric or boracic acid.

Kursanov (1956b) states that phosphates, starch phosphorylase, and a weakly active invertase have been detected in the fibrovascular bundles of sugar beet. This is in distinct contrast with the reports of Wanner (1953) for phloem exudate of *Robinia* and of Rouschal (1941) for squash.

Kursanov's observation of a uniform sugar level along the paths of conduction was made on the sugar beet. If his analyses involved principally the petiole, his observation is understandable because the establishment of the concentration in sugar beet occurs in the lamina of the leaf in the bundle ends and the small veins. Lowering of concentration, if it occurs at all, takes place in the phloem strands in the root adjacent to the actual storage cells. There is no reason for a gradient in concentration along the petiole, for this organ uses little sugar and it probably synthesizes enough for its own activity. In the growing beet root there is no occasion for a lowering of concentration in the root as the total volume and contents of the phloem stream are utilized by the growing cells. Although Kursanov and his associates have made excellent use of radioactive elements—particularly C^{14}—in translocation studies, they seem to have little or no appreciation of the anatomical relations of phloem tissues. Hence, as Esau *et al.* (1957) point out, many of their experiments have little relevance to the problem they are studying.

Zimmerman (1960) has written an excellent review of the subject of transport in the phloem. He covers recent work in Europe and the United States, including the experiments on phloem exudate collected by means of the mouth parts of insects, and interprets the bulk of the recent work as confirming the mass-flow mechanism.

chapter three Movement of Viruses, Indicators, Growth Regulators, and Radioactive Tracers

MOVEMENT OF VIRUSES

As was the case with food movement in plants, early works on virus movement were not consistent and workers disagreed in their interpretations. In a review in 1939 (Crafts, 1939b) it was pointed out that three basic concepts are essential to an understanding of virus movement:

(1) Viruses vary in their tissue relations: some thrive and multiply in parenchyma and vascular tissues, others are strictly localized in the phloem.

(2) Plants differ with respect to their rates of food transport, their responses to manipulation in experimental procedures, and their reaction to virus infection. Food and virus movements are slow in tobacco, rapid in sugar beet (Bennett, 1938). When tobacco leaves are shaded they export their food reserves, turn yellow, and abscise, whereas shaded beet leaves draw reserves from the root and persist for days. Thus, shaded tobacco leaves act as sources for export of foods and virus, beet leaves as sinks. Curly-top virus produces

pronounced symptoms on susceptible varieties of beets, mild symptoms on resistant varieties.

(3) A clearer view of food transport is needed. Symplastic movement from palisade to phloem and out again to sinks in cambium, storage, and meristematic parenchyma is common to all plants. It probably involves diffusion accelerated by protoplasmic streaming and may include a polarized concentration mediated by metabolism.

Rapid movement of foods and viruses implies specialization of both structure and function of the conducting tissues; the sieve tubes form the conduits but the mechanism of movement still lacks adequate description. Virus studies provide critical evidence upon which to judge existing theories.

Bauer (1906a, b) performed classical experiments on infectious chlorosis, showing it to be transmissible only by grafting. Davis (1929) showed that short days and defoliation would reduce and eliminate chlorosis from *Abutilon*.

Bennett (1927) made the first comprehensive studies on virus movement as affected by ringing, shading, and pruning. In 1924 he proved that curl virus of raspberry could be held above a ring throughout the season of treatment whereas unringed shoots transmitted the virus to the roots and to newly developing shoots. Bennett concluded that movement of the curl virus showed a correlation with food translocation.

Severin (1924) recorded rates of movement of curly-top virus in sugar beets as high as 18 cm in 30 minutes, and Storey (1928) showed downward movement of maize streak of 10 cm in one hour and 40 cm in two hours. These are above the recorded rates of protoplasmic streaming.

Further studies on curly-top virus by Bennett (1934, 1935, 1937) and by Bennett and Esau (1936) proved that the relation between virus movement and food transport through phloem becomes more strict with more careful experimentation. Bennett measured movement of 1.25 cm per hour in tobacco stem and of 15 cm in 6 minutes in sugar beet leaves.

Of great interest were observations that virus could be found in segments of tobacco stem separated from the point of infection by virus-free segments (Bennett, 1934); that the virus occurs in high concentration in phloem exudate of sugar beet (Bennett, 1935); that virus moved into the phloem of seed coats to an extremely high concentration against a virus gradient during food storage in the seed (Bennett and Esau, 1936); and that in a three-crowned beet plant having a common tap root, virus showed a critical partition, moving rapidly into darkened or defoliated crowns but avoiding leafy crowns that were actively synthesizing foods (Bennett, 1937).

From the accumulated work on movement of curly-top virus Bennett (1937) concluded that virus movement bears no relation to virus multiplication or to virus concentration gradients but is correlated with food movement, and that the behavior of virus in the plant supports the theory of mass movement in the phloem. The localized viruses are ideal as indicators of food movement because they are introduced into the phloem with a minimum of injury by insects feeding in sieve tubes. It is practically impossible to introduce virus, dyes, or any other indicators into sieve tubes by physiological means, for these elements operate as inflated osmotic systems and the indicators are rapidly washed away from the point of introduction by phloem exudation.

Bennett (1938, 1940b) also worked on nonlocalized viruses, reporting on sugar-beet mosaic and tobacco mosaic. Bringing from his earlier work critical technics and a full appreciation of differences not only in viruses but also in test plants, he gave a comprehensive picture of virus movement. Sugar-beet mosaic travels faster than curly top because it moves in both sieve tubes and parenchyma. Basipetal movement of tobacco mosaic exceeded acropetal movement in horizontal stems having basal suckers (sinks) and a group of leaves at the main stem apex (source). The reverse was true of plants maturing seeds in the main stem apex.

In vegetative plants acropetal movement was hastened by shading and defoliation. Basipetal movement was very slow in main stems in the dark. Roots of Turkish tobacco were susceptible to infection but a long period elapsed between inoculation of roots and appearance of symptoms on the tops. Defoliation hastened the upward movement. Rings on the stems of Turkish tobacco plants delayed passage of mosaic virus. In *Nicotiana glauca* plants ringed to break phloem continuity, virus failed to pass the ring in periods up to 250 days. In such plants tobacco mosaic virus is virtually restricted to the phloem. Cucumber mosaic, on the other hand, was able to pass such rings, but passage was delayed.

Evidently, movement of nonlocalized viruses in plants is of two types: (1) a slow cell-to-cell movement in relatively unspecialized parenchyma; and (2) a rapid movement through the phloem.

Bennett (1940a) reviewed the relations of viruses to plant tissues, particularly those of localization and translocation. He pointed out that viruses restricted to parenchyma are less common than other types because they are less readily disseminated. Phloem-limited viruses are somewhat more common; movement may be very rapid. Viruses of the mosaic type that occur in both mesophyll parenchyma and in phloem are extremely common.

In a paper on the relation of food movement to virus movement Bennett (1940b) made a comparative study of tobacco-mosaic and curly-top viruses. In *N. glauca* plants having top and basal grafts of Turkish tobacco 3 feet apart, virus moved from the top to the basal graft and produced symptoms in 6 to 9 days. In 7 out of 10 plants movement in the reverse direction failed for periods of 224 to 252 days. Upward movement was relatively rapid when the tops were defoliated. Bennett found that movement was out of shaded mature tobacco leaves, whereas it was into young shaded shoots of tobacco and leaves of sugar beet. He concluded that the rapid movement of tobacco-mosaic virus is correlated with food transport and that the factors involved in the movement are not different from those responsible for movements of other viruses.

Rapid transmission of the virus diseases of peach rosette, rosette mosaic, and mosaic, and a yellow disease of cherry was shown by Hildebrand (1942) to be induced by inserting diseased buds midway on the stem of peach seedlings 12 to 24 inches tall and cutting off the stem one node above the diseased bud. This technic reduces the time required for expression of symptoms from one year to about one month. Grafting was effective on cherries, plums, and peaches, and whip grafting resulted in production of ring-spot symptoms on sour cherry in 14 days. Hildebrand interprets these responses on the basis that the virus moves bodily through the plant in the assimilate stream. Contact periods only long enough to provide a callus bridge are required, but normally the virus is carried down into the roots where symptoms are not expressed. Severely pruning the top of the plant to stimulate rapid growth causes virus to be carried into new shoots where symptoms appear rapidly. Hildebrand and Curtis (1942) showed that darkening or shading will induce entrance of virus and development of symptoms, even in mature leaves. With Bennett, they agree that viruses are transported in plants with food materials.

Bennett (1943) showed that the viruses of ring spot and cucumber mosaic will pass a newly made graft more rapidly than will curly top. In short contact periods the ring spot often moved ahead of cucumber mosaic. Bennett thinks that ring spot can move through meristematic cells, cucumber mosaic thrives best in differentiated parenchyma, and curly top moves only through mature phloem. Passage, therefore, was in the order of establishment of these three types of tissue in the graft union.

Bennett (1944) made extensive studies on dodder transmission of plant viruses. He concluded that viruses appear to be acquired by dodder mainly by movement, along with food materials, from the host into the parasite through the phloem. Concerning movement from dodder to host plant Bennett pictures two mechanisms: first, occasional phloem transport resulting from reversal of the normal direction of food movement; and second, by passage from the parenchyma of the haustorium into that of the host through plasmodesmata. Lackey (1948) found that, like the beet leafhopper, dodder haustoria are attracted to the vascular bundles of the beet petiole.

Pierce's disease of grape and alfalfa studied by Houston, Esau, and Hewitt (1947) proved to be a new type of virus disease. The virus causing these diseases is transmitted by insects of the leafhopper type and apparently is limited to the xylem. The feeding punctures terminate in the tracheary elements and rate studies show movement at 10 cm per hour, indicating movement in the transpiration stream.

Zech (1952) suggested that the accelerated movement of virus in plants may result from two mechanisms. Upon inoculation, tobacco mosaic moves slowly, then more rapidly in the elongated parenchyma cells of the veins, and finally at even higher rates in sieve tubes. He cites rates of 0.18 mm per hour in epidermis between the veins, 0.4 mm per hour in elongated epidermis along the veins, and 8 mm per hour in elongated bundle sheath cells.

Zech noted the discontinuous distribution of infection during the early systemic movement along the stem, as had Bennett and others. Zech explained this as resulting from movement of the virus, not as complete molecules but as smaller noninfective precursory particles. He considered whole virus particles as too large to pass through plasmodesmata. The current concept that the virus particles consist of cores of DNA surrounded by protein may lend some basis for Zech's concept. As Esau, Currier, and Cheadle (1957) point out, the connecting strands of the sieve plates are large enough to allow passage of virus particles, but plasmodesmata in side walls may not be. The movement of viruses, they stress, is merely a part of the problem of translocation of materials in the phloem.

INDICATORS

From early studies Schumacher (1930, 1937) concluded that fluorescein, applied to veins in droplets of gelatin, moved in sieve tubes by a molecular mechanism and independent of solvent. Palmquist (1939) showed that in well-watered red kidney bean plants fluorescein would move basipetally from a dipped terminal leaflet and would enter lateral leaflets. It failed to pass scalded petioles of well-watered plants; in water-deficient plants it passed, flowing downward through the xylem to the stem.

Schumacher observed that fluorescein accumulated in the parietal cytoplasm of *Pelargonium* sieve tubes; Mason and Phillis (1937) were unable to confirm his results. Rhodes (1937) concluded that fluorescein moved in the xylem, whereas Palmquist showed that it may move in both xylem and phloem. No one has proved that it may move rapidly in sieve tubes independently of foods.

Rouschal (1941) described studies with fluorescein on several tree species and on *Pelargonium* and *Cucurbita pepo*. He found fluorescein to be strongly absorbed by the cytoplasm of the sieve tubes, companion cells, and phloem parenchyma. It was also detectable in the vacuoles. Rouschal concluded that the dye moves by a mass streaming in low concentration in the vacuoles of the sieve elements and is accumulated secondarily by the cytoplasm. He found fluorescein movement to parallel food movement; it could be reversed by drastic treatment with plasmolyzing agents.

In a review Schumacher (1947) reaffirmed his conviction that fluorescein moves in cells, independent of the solvent and independent of protoplasmic streaming. He believes that fluorescein movement in sieve tubes takes place in the plasma, but he concluded that further questions concerning mechanism must await solution of the mysteries of the protoplasm.

Bauer (1949) studied fluorescein movement in leaves of *Elodea densa, Ranunculus aquatilis,* and *Bryonia diocia* and found rapid movement to take place along cell walls with subsequent accumulation in cytoplasm. In vascular bundles rapid movement took place in phloem walls. He found that with increased concentrations the dye appeared in the vacuoles of the sieve tubes and he concluded that inorganic salts could be conducted in the sieve tubes, which assumption he confirmed by tests with KCNS. Bauer found that primulin, Rhodamin B, Rhodamin 6G, and chinin chloride moved in sieve tubes.

He also found that berberin sulfate and potassium fluorescein would move in the same sieve tube. Watching such movement under the microscope he found that movement always involved first a diffuse spreading of the dyes in vacuoles followed by accumulation in the cytoplasm.

In a later paper Bauer (1953) studied the mechanics of dye movement. Using detached leaves and petioles of *Pelargonium,* he varied many factors in order to bring about measurable changes in the rate and direction of movement. He concluded that the driving force for movement was situated in the leaf blade, particularly in the bundle ends where sucrose may be secreted into the sieve tubes by the parenchyma cells that are rich in phosphatases. In spite of a previous belief that sieve-tube conduction involves electric polarity and that the sieve elements act as a series of microglands (1949), he came to the conviction that the mass-flow theory best explained his results with dyes.

Schumacher and Hulsbruch (1955) disagree with Bauer's conclusions and severely criticize his technics. They point out the difficulty of explaining mass flow across sieve plates, a criticism that is still valid.

Eschrich (1953) has done some interesting work with fluorescein in *Impatiens.* When he severed a bundle in the stem of this plant he could see the dye move out of the bundle into the parenchyma surrounding the wound. Soon new sieve tubes differentiated from adjacent bundles by dedifferentiation of parenchyma and made connection with the wounded bundle. The dye then moved through the newly constituted sieve-tube system and once again became limited to the sieve tubes and their companion cells. Eschrich pointed out that transport of the dye through the reconstituted vascular bundles started before the loss of nuclei from the sieve-tube cells and he cautioned against a rigid relation between function and a particular structural state in sieve elements.

GROWTH REGULATORS

Early work on growth-regulator movement involved mainly polar transport of auxin (Went and Thimann, 1937). Skoog (1938) by careful studies showed that indole acetic acid may move in the plant by three distinct mechanisms: (1) Endogenous auxin or indole acetic acid applied in physiological concentration undergoes a basipetal polar transport. In order to reverse such movement, concentrations ranging from 100 to 1000 times as great must be used (Went, 1937; Went and White, 1939). (2) Auxin applied through the culture solution is absorbed and moved upward in the transpiration stream. (3) Auxin applied in high concentration in lanolin to upper portions of squash stems was found to move downward and accumulate above a killed portion of the stem. Skoog concluded that this movement was via the phloem.

Although Skoog found no auxin in phloem exudate of squash, Huber, Schmidt, and Jahnel (1937) report auxin in varying concentrations in phloem exudate from different trees.

There is much physiological work indicating that flowering in plants is induced by a substance synthesized at a distance from the point of induction. Stout (1945), studying translocation of the flower-inducing stimulus in sugar beet, found that it moved down a donor shoot in the light and up into a darkened shoot that was in contact through the lower root with the donor shoot. It would not move up into a third attached illuminated shoot. This movement indicates that the flower-inducing substance, like curly-top virus, is translocated along with food materials.

A tremendous number of growth-regulating compounds have been studied during the past 15 years, of which 2,4-D is the most prominent. This compound proved to be an excellent translocation indicator, for, following its application to one leaf of a bean seedling, bending of the epicotyl followed and thus an indication of transport was obtained on intact plants.

Mitchell and Brown (1946), Rice (1948), Linder, Brown, and Mitchell (1949), Rohrbaugh and Rice (1949), and Weintraub and Brown (1950) proved that 2,4-D movement in bean took place only when assimilates were moving from the treated leaf into the epicotyl. Davis and Smith (1950) found translocation in bean to depend on carbohydrate, and Day (1952) carried out exhaustive studies on the velocity and direction of 2,4-D movement in bean and on various factors influencing it. He proved that 2,4-D is an ideal indicator for translocation studies and he concluded that this compound is moved in plants by the same mechanism that transports naturally occurring food materials. Most of the translocation studies involving 2,4-D carried out since 1950 have involved radioactive forms. These will be considered next.

RADIOACTIVE TRACERS

The production of radioactive isotopes ushered in a new era in physiological research on translocation. They provided the long-sought tracers that could be used in whole, intact plants, and since their introduction more real knowledge of normal transport processes has been acquired than in all the preceding years.

Use of these tracers in animal physiology followed their discovery, and their application in plant work came soon after that. Stout and Hoagland (1939) demonstrated that radioactive phosphorus (P^{32}) absorbed by roots moves upward through the plant but that lateral movement is so rapid that ordinary analyses of wood and bark, fractionated after the element had moved up through the stem, showed the presence of tracer in both tissues. Only by separating bark and wood with an impervious barrier of oiled paper were they able to demonstrate that movement was occurring in the wood.

Biddulph (1940) worked with P^{32} in bean plants. Adding the tracer to the nutrient solution of large plants, he studied its uptake and movement after absorption periods of one, two, and four hours. The plants were removed from the culture medium, fractionated, dried, and analyzed by GM counting. At the end of one hour the tracer was found only in the roots; after two hours it was present in hypocotyl and stem; after four hours a water extract of the roots equaled in concentration the culture solution and the tracer was present in the tips of the shoots. The concentration in the fourth and fifth leaves was greater than in the stem and lower leaves, possibly as a result of secondary movement in the phloem. Biddulph concluded that movement was rapid and that it took place in the transpiration stream.

Later Biddulph (1941) studied diurnal migration of injected P^{32} from bean leaves. Injection was done by cutting a flap involving the principal lateral vein in the terminal leaflet of the second alternate leaf. Dissection was done under water and the dissected flap, cut so that the tracer solution flowed into the leaf in an acropetal direction, was allowed to absorb P^{32} solution for five minutes and was then transferred to distilled water. After four-hour migration periods the plants were cut into fractions, dried, ashed, and counted. From preliminary trials it was found that the tracer spread rapidly through the treated leaf and then migrated down the petiole into the stem, some of it going acropetally into upper leaves, most of it moving downward into lower leaves, stem, and roots.

Because time experiments indicated a possible daily cycle in the migration of phosphate, Biddulph designed some experiments to explore the response during a 24-hour period. These showed that most of the phosphate migrated during the daytime—a maximum around 10 A.M. and a minimum around 10 P.M. Migration from the petiole was principally downward, only a small portion moving upward in the morning. The amount of P^{32} injected into a leaf during one of these experiments was of the same order as the amount normally moving into a leaf in 24 hours. During the morning, when migration was rapid, some of the tracer possibly migrated into the phloem where it passed acropetally into the upper leaves. Biddulph concluded that P^{32} may move upward in the xylem to the leaves, where it passes over into the phloem and moves back downward; thus a circulation of phosphorus in the plant is possible.

Colwell (1942a, b) studied the translocation of radiophosphorus in squash plants and found that great care must be exercised to control uptake and movement if transport by a single tissue system is desired. He found that if he applied the tracer in large volume to a leaf it would move through the intact leaf into the xylem and migrate along hydrostatic gradients toward the roots and toward the short tips. On the other hand, if he applied the tracer in small volume to a relatively small portion of leaf, or used plants growing in a saturated atmosphere, he could limit export to the phloem. Scalding of petioles was used as a control on the tissue utilized for transport. When transport was restricted to the phloem, movement of the tracer was predominately in the direction of food movement.

Biddulph and Markle (1944) used the leaf-injection method (Biddulph, 1941) to study the translocation of P^{32} in the phloem of cotton plants. Although this injection method resulted in rapid uptake through the xylem of the treated leaf (almost the entire leaf contained the tracer after a five-minute absorption period), under the conditions of their tests the tracer apparently migrated rapidly into the phloem where it moved out of the leaf into the bark of the stem above and below the axil of the treated leaf. The tracer was followed along the veins to the petiole and on into the stem. As it entered the stem its distribution resulted in concentration gradients extending both up and down from the point of entry. Downward movement was in excess of 21 cm per hour. The tracer in moving from the leaf via the phloem diffused readily into the xylem, and its primary movement in the phloem was proved by separating the bark from the wood by oiled paper as in the experiments of Stout and Hoagland. Under normal conditions it seems possible for phosphorus, transported in the phloem, to migrate in the xylem of stem or root and reascend the stem into the leaves, maintaining a circuit in the plant. This is logical in view of its known role in the metabolism of all living cells.

From the distribution pattern of their tracers in the cotton stem Biddulph and Markle suggested that the movement is analogous to diffusion. Contending that the mass-flow hypothesis postulated a unidirectional movement, they stated that such a mechanism could not explain the simultaneous upward and downward movement of tracer that they observed. Theirs is a misinterpretation of the hypothesis, however, because mass flow from a leaf might split and move to two separate sinks just as water flows from a single pipe through a T-connection. They found upward movement to be quite variable, running from little to 40 percent of the mobile phosphate. This is readily explained on the basis of variation between crown and roots in balance of utilization, which reflects differing rates of root and shoot growth.

Rabideau and Burr (1945) used radioactive carbon as a tracer in translocation studies. When leaves were exposed to $C^{14}O_2$, photosynthesis resulted in formation of carbohydrates that moved both upward and downward in plants. This labeled photosynthate would not pass killed portions of stems, indicating movement in the phloem. P^{32} applied to roots passed readily upward past killed portions of the stem.

Withner (1949) studied distribution of P^{32} in maturing corn plants by applying the tracer to roots as phosphate. The tracer increased throughout the plants for about two weeks after introduction to the culture medium; then it gradually decreased. In foliage, the concentration approached a constant value on a dry weight basis. Whereas concentration lowered in all the reproductive parts, it remained relatively high in the seeds, intermediate in husks, and low in cobs and tassels. After its primary distribution through the transpiration stream this element apparently undergoes secondary movement in the phloem, along with foods.

Radioactive tracers are being used in ever-increasing amounts in contemporary plant physiological research. Because many of the newer researches involve technics and ideas with which the writer is working, the more recent papers will be considered along with results to be presented in later sections. Certainly, use of these elements is placing translocation research on a much sounder basis than could the older ringing experiments and analytical methods. Many labeled compounds when applied to the outer surfaces of leaves are absorbed through the cuticle, moved to the vascular tissues, and then transported to distant parts of the plant at high rates. Because such tests involve nontoxic compounds, intact plants, and critical methods of preparation, the answers they give are true pictures of the normal functioning of plants. Even such results, however, are subject to varying interpretations by different plant physiologists.

SECTION TWO

Uptake of Water and Salts by Roots

chapter four

The Concept of Accumulation; Mechanics and Requirements

THE CONCEPT OF ACCUMULATION

The uptake and movement of water and salts by plants was studied in very early times. Stephen Hales (1769) performed many experiments in which he measured the amount of water transpired by plants, weighing the water in given volumes of soil and relating this to the amount lost by plants. He also studied the uptake of water by roots and excised branches.

Textbooks of botany in the latter nineteenth century described plant roots and their functions of water and salt absorption, but little was known of mechanism until the work of Dixon and Joly (1894). The contributions of Strasburger, Renner, Ursprung, and Bode have been cited. With the general acceptance of the tensile strength of water and the function of transpiration pull, the uptake and movement of water by plants seemed to fall within a logical and understandable pattern.

One phenomenon that has interested plant physiologists since early times is root pressure as manifested by guttation, bleeding, and xylem exudation from excised root systems. Priestley (1920) visualized a mechanism to explain root pressure. He stressed the fact that water and salts may permeate the root tissues, diffusing along the cell walls until they reach the Casparian strip, a region in the radial walls of the endodermis layer that is impregnated with fatty materials. Across the endodermis Priestley pictured a differential permeability resulting from a gradient of acidity, the xylem being more acid than the phloem or the cortex. On the basis of this polarized permeability gradient and the accumulating power of the cortex he proposed that solutes and water absorbed by the cortex are released into the xylem vessels and that this solution moves upward and is manifested as xylem exudation. Organic matter in the xylem sap Priestley attributed to the differentiating xylem tracheal elements.

Understanding of the role of mineral elements in the nutrition of plants had been slowly evolving since the work of Lavoisier, Ingenhousz, and Senebier (Russell, 1927). De Saussure, basing studies on these earlier works, found that mineral elements are incorporated into plants as is carbon, that nitrates and other mineral elements are essential to plant growth, and that nitrogen utilized by plants comes from the soil and not from the atmosphere. He pointed out that plants absorb much more water from the soil than they require for their growth and that they absorb certain mineral elements from the soil that they do not require; also, that plants absorb minerals from the soil in proportions different from their occurrence in the soil solution.

Woodward (1699) first grew plants in water culture and proved that growth in river water and soil extract was superior to growth in rain water. Sachs reintroduced the method in 1860 and proved its usefulness for plant physiological investigation.

Liebig was responsible for overthrowing the humus theory of plant nutrition and he proved that mineral elements essential to plant growth were largely derived from the soil. He thought that both carbon dioxide and nitrogen were obtained from the air and he engaged in bitter polemics with Lawes and Gilbert, the British investigators who set up the Rothamsted Experiment Station in England. Liebig was responsible for establishing the great usefulness of phosphate fertilizers but it remained for others to establish the role of nitrates in plant nutrition.

Introduction of the use of mineral fertilizers in agriculture was followed by a period of great activity that saw the establishment of test plots on which fertilizers were used in different amounts and proportions; these plots were developed in great numbers and in many agricultural regions. Emphasis was on increasing yields of crops, however, and little attention was paid to the mechanism by which plants obtained the nutrients from the soil.

Plant physiologists meanwhile were attacking the problem of the active absorption of ions. Osterhout (1922) found that the sap in the large-celled alga *Valonia* contains 40 times as much KCl as the sea water in which it grows whereas NaCl in the cells is less than in sea water; $MgSO_4$ is also less.

In a memorable paper, Hoagland and Davis (1923) reported on experiments with fresh-water alga *Nitella*. Squeezing vacuolar sap from large individual cells, they analyzed for the common ions known to be present and compared the results with the analysis of the pond water in which the plants were growing. Table 4-1, which gives data from their paper, illustrates the results.

Table 4-1

Analysis of *Nitella* Sap and of Pond Water

	Specific resistance ohms	Freezing point depression	pH	K ppm	Na ppm	Ca ppm	Mg ppm	Cl ppm	SO_4 ppm	PO_4 ppm	NO_3 ppm
Sap from largest cells	82.3	0.465° C	5.2	2120	230	410	430	3220	800	350	0
Pond water	2050.0	0.018° C	7.2–9.4	*	5	31	41	32	31	0.4	34
Factor of concentration	25	26			46	13	10	100	26	870	

* No weighable precipitate of potassium chloroplatinate from 200 cc of water.

From Table 4-1 it is evident that every element determined in the sap with the exception of nitrogen was present in very much higher concentration than in the pond water but that the factors of concentration were very different for the different elements. Potassium, chlorine, and sodium have higher relative values than sulfate, calcium, and magnesium. The potassium concentration in the pond water was undoubtedly very low and phosphate was just detectable.

On the basis of the conductivity measurement Hoagland and

Davis concluded that the inorganic elements in *Nitella* sap exist mainly in the ionic state; 80 to 90 percent of the positive ions could be balanced by negative ions with the remainder possibly balanced by organic acid anions. Insoluble or combined elements found in the cell wall or protoplasm included calcium, magnesium, sulfur, silicon, iron, and aluminum. Calcium was predominant; potassium

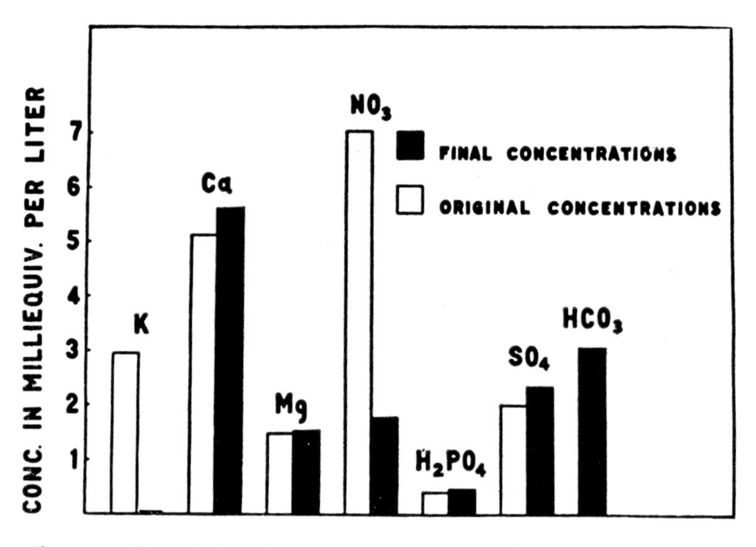

Fig. 4-1. The relation of water and solute absorption as shown by barley plants (duplicate sets of 168) grown for 19 days in a complete culture solution. (From Hoagland, 1936)

was not present. The pH of the cell sap was constant at about 5.2 and this value did not change when the culture medium was varied through the range pH 5.0 to 9.0. Nitrate ion was found to be absorbed by *Nitella* more rapidly than the cations in the medium.

Hoagland (1944) and his associates carried on a very active program of investigation of the phenomena of salt and water uptake by plants of various kinds. Fig. 4-1 shows the changes in concentration of nutrients in a water culture of barley plants during a 24-hour absorption period.

It is evident in the figure that potassium was completely taken out of the solution during the 24-hour period and nitrate reduced to about 25 percent of the original concentration whereas calcium, magnesium, phosphate, and sulfate were removed more slowly than water. The bicarbonate appeared, presumably as a result of aerobic respiration.

From a great amount of work on the accumulation of salts by plant roots (Hoagland and Broyer, 1936) and potato discs (Steward, 1935), Hoagland (1937) makes the important conclusion that salt accumulation is dependent on metabolic activities of plant cells associated with respiration and reflected in CO_2 production.

MECHANICS OF ACCUMULATION AND ROOT PRESSURE

Crafts (1936), working with Broyer, collected xylem exudate from excised squash roots growing in aerated culture solution in the greenhouse. In 24 hours 551.7 ml of sap were collected from a root weighing 450 grams. Evidently the xylem elements of this root were emptied many times during the collection. In 1938 these experiments were repeated (Crafts and Broyer, 1938) and a mechanism to explain the migration of salts and water into roots was proposed.

Two squash plants were used in the sap collections. These had grown for 55 days in full aerated Hoagland's solution in the greenhouse. Table 4-2 presents the results.

Table 4-2

Fresh and Dry Weights of Xylem Exudate from Squash

	Weight of roots		Volume of exudate		
	Fresh	Dry	0–1 hrs	0–24 hrs	24–48 hrs
	g	g	ml	ml	ml
Plant No. 1	81.7	3.4		243	100
Plant No. 2	136.0	5.8	40	343	140

The nitrate concentration of the xylem exudate was more than twice that of the culture solution during the early stages of the experiment and decreased to an equal concentration after the first 24 hours. Measurements on the cross-sectional area of the open lumina of the xylem conduits of squash roots in the absorbing region and above prove that the volume of such conducting elements constitutes approximately 1 percent of the total volume of the roots. From this it can be calculated that the open xylem elements of root number 1 had their contents displaced over 300 times during the 24-hour collection period. Root number 2 had its contents displaced 30 times during the first hour and over 250 times during the first 24-hour collection period. Even though the dry weight composition of this xylem exudate varies from 0.21 to 0.59 percent, it seems highly improbable that even this small amount of material could be derived from the differentiating xylem elements of the growing root tips (Priestley, 1920).

The mechanism proposed by Crafts and Broyer to explain uptake of water and salts by roots is based on experimental results from many sources and on a clear picture of the active root in the absorbing region (Crafts and Broyer, 1938). Experiments by Hoagland and his associates have proved that xylem exudate from active roots may contain all of the mineral elements normally absorbed by plants, and often these are higher in concentration in the sap than in the culture solution (Hoagland, 1936; Hoagland and Broyer, 1936). Water and salts may enter the root simultaneously and they are released into the xylem vessels together; salts may enter the xylem faster than water, or slower; where the rate of entry exceeds that of water, work is evidently being done at the expense of respirational energy. Hoagland (1936) stresses the fact that no matter what the concentration of solutes in the nutrient medium these solutes are not physiologically available unless oxygen is supplied to roots, and carbon dioxide removed, at necessary rates.

Fig. 4-2 shows the effect of aeration on accumulation of salt by excised roots of barley plants.

Furthermore, since energy exchanges are involved in accumulation processes, a supply of available carbohydrates must be furnished to root cells; hence synthesis and translocation of sugars are interrelated with mineral nutrition. Finally, the metabolic processes associated with accumulation must be maintained at a certain minimal rate in order that the cells may retain solutes accumulated in the sap. In the absence of adequate aeration roots have been shown to lose solutes, but these may be regained if aeration is renewed. In fact, the cycle of accumulation and loss may be repeated several times without injury to roots by manipulating the oxygen supply.

Fig. 4-3 shows a cross section of the root of squash in the region of absorption. Tissues external to the endodermis in its primary condition have prominent intercellular spaces and thin cell walls. All cells are in contact with the culture medium by way of the continuous cell wall phase, the apoplast (Münch, 1930). Water imbibed by these walls constitutes a continuum through which ions may diffuse to satisfy differences in concentration such as are established by rapid accumulation.

Cells of the endodermis in its primary condition in this region have suberized Casparian strips that effectively prevent leakage of solution under pressure from inside the stele. Tissues inside the endodermis are small celled and tightly packed and lack intercellular spaces.

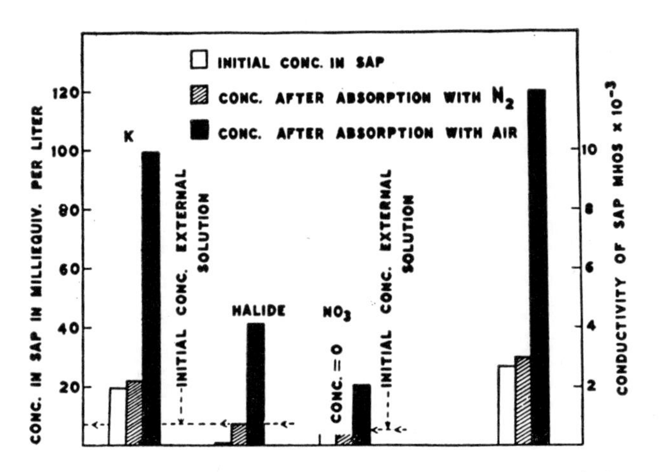

Fig. 4-2. The effect of aeration on accumulation of salt by excised roots of barley plants. (From Hoagland, 1936)

Plasmodesmata are known to occur through the closing membranes of all pits between living parenchyma cells. Consequently, the symplast (Münch, 1930) of the root must constitute an interconnected protoplasmic unit, and movement of solutes within the symplast must take place readily, being accelerated within cells by protoplasmic streaming and going on between cells by diffusion along the plasmodesmata.

In contrast with this protoplasmic unity, anatomical features of the root designate two tissue systems that are physiologically distinct. These are: (1) the cortex, in direct contact with the culture medium and aerated by the elaborate system of intercellular spaces present; and (2) the stele, which contains the vascular strands, the phloem, and the xylem and which receives its salts and oxygen from the solution that has passed through the cortex. Foods are delivered to the root cells through the phloem and distributed via the symplast. Water and salts destined to move to the top of the plant via the xylem are supplied to the stele only after they have passed through the cortex and endodermis. Cortical cells have the first opportunity to absorb oxygen and minerals from the environment.

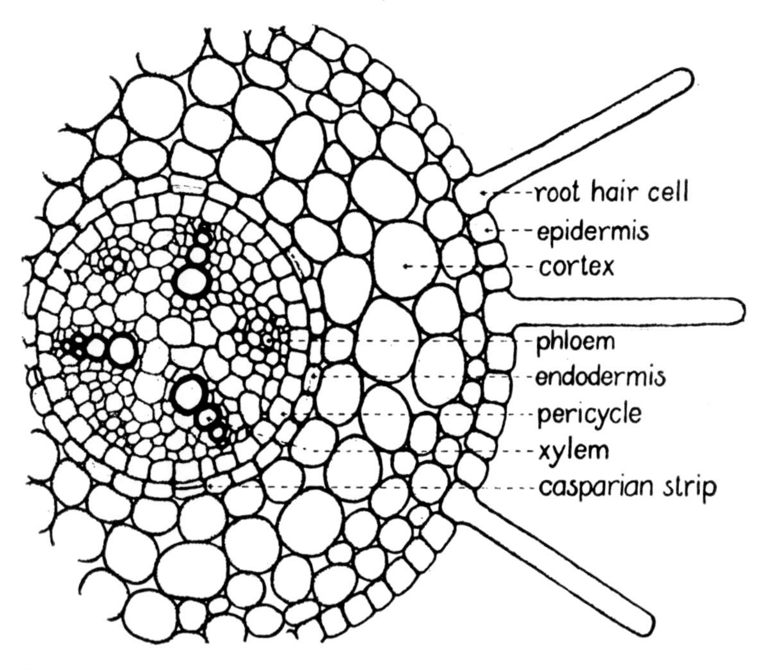

Fig. 4-3. Semidiagrammatic drawing of a young squash root in the region of maximum absorption, showing cortex, endodermis, pericycle, and stele.

Stellar tissues may pass the minerals on to the xylem; they have second choice with respect to oxygen. Furthermore, they are exposed to products of metabolism of all the growing and absorbing region. They are bound within a cell layer capable of withstanding internal pressure but relatively impervious to oxygen. They surround the nonliving xylem elements (apoplast) that constitute the only channels of escape for a solution under pressure, and the path of least resistance for sap under tension.

The structure of the root imposes upon the cortical cells of the absorbing region an environment favoring maximum growth and accumulation accompanied by a high metabolic activity. The living cells surrounding the xylem vessels of this region, however, exist in an environment tending toward a lower level of cell activity and to favor, in contrast with the cortex, loss of solutes. Protoplasmic continuity should by streaming and diffusion tend to maintain equal concentrations of ions across these layers. The net result should be that, following absorption in the cortex, ions pass inward along the symplast in concentrations that cells inside the Casparian strip cannot maintain, resulting in loss into the xylem. Structure indicates a gradient of decreasing O_2 and increasing CO_2 from the cortex of the root to the stele. Root behavior indicates an activity gradient in the protoplasm of the root paralleling this O_2:CO_2 gradient and presumably conditioned by it. Although permeability may be conditioned by cumulative effects of environmental factors such as temperature, concentrations, or regulating chemicals, the mechanism described should continue to function so long as the activity gradient is maintained.

Ions released into the apoplast of the stele cannot move out again because of the impervious Casparian strip. Because all cells of the root are in osmotic equilibrium with the soil solution, water from the cortex must move in to satisfy the osmotic gradient across the endodermis; solution in the apoplast of the stele must develop hydrostatic pressure. Seeking the pathway of least resistance, this solution should follow the apoplast to the xylem vessels and move upward. It is this solution, less concentrated than vacuolar sap but more concentrated than the culture medium, that appears at the cut end of the excised root system in the form of xylem exudate.

This exudation is not an abnormal flow, contingent upon cutting, for if the top of the plant is enclosed and the atmosphere allowed to become saturated, solution of like concentration and in like volume appears in droplets at the hydathodes and drips from the plant. Concentrations of various ions in the exuded sap need bear no obvious relation to those of the culture (Hoagland, 1936), the amounts and proportions of ions released depending upon relative rates of absorption and the ability of the cells of various tissues to retain them.

If migration of salts in roots involves an activity gradient in their tissues, the essential features of the proposed mechanism should be reconcilable with known root structure and function, and certain relations should be subject to quantitative determination. Structural relations, on the other hand, do not readily submit to quantitative experimentation, and the criterion for judging these depends upon the degree to which the known structures fit the mechanical requirements imposed by the functions performed. Final acceptance of any mechanism must rely not only upon chemical analyses but also upon anatomical studies and finally upon an integration of all available information with respect to the performance of the root system. A few relevant issues will be discussed.

OXYGEN SUPPLY

There are three obvious sources of oxygen to roots: (1) the soil, including the soil atmosphere and dissolved oxygen in the soil solution; (2) the shoot system of the plant, provided it is close enough so that conduction through the intercellular space system of the cortex may be effective; and (3) the anion supply, consisting principally of absorbed nitrate and secondarily of sulfate.

The oxygen-supplying power of the soil has long been recognized and horticultural practices have included drainage and tillage designed to aerate the soil; likewise, aeration of culture solution has become popular as a means of providing conditions for maximum solute uptake.

The importance of the internal supply of oxygen has been pointed out by Cannon (1932). It should receive increasing attention as the role of root respiration is more widely recognized. There seems little doubt that the oxygen released into the intercellular space system as a result of photosynthesis may move through the cortical tissues to the root system, at least in low-growing herbaceous plants. Many of our highest producing crop plants are of such nature. The solubility relations of O_2 and CO_2 indicate that in aquatics an actual pressure flow may be established. Many such plants have specialized intercellular space systems consisting of open passageways through their leaves, stems, and roots. The well-known evolution of oxygen by *Elodea* is an example of the free movement of oxygen gas. If such free oxygen is absorbed by roots and CO_2 is released, the latter will remain in solution and move with the water stream. Gas from the leaves must immediately move down to satisfy the pressure deficit so created, bringing about an effective pressure flow. Thus photosynthesis may provide both carbohydrates and oxygen for use by roots.

That the reduction of nitrates in roots may provide oxygen for respiration has not been widely recognized. Arnon (1937) has shown the importance of this supply by comparing ammonia and nitrate as sources of nitrogen. Barley plants growing in culture solution of C. P. salts with ammonia as a nitrogen source required either forced aeration or a supplement of certain microelements, particularly manganese or copper, to produce yields comparable with those of plants grown in solution containing nitrate.

The interrelations of these three oxygen sources is of interest. Cannon (1932) found with roots in water that oxygen absorption from the culture medium was practically stopped during periods of illumination. In the absence of rapid solute absorption, the internal supply was adequate for respiration. When Arnon (1937) supplied nitrate to barley plants in shallow water culture, forced aeration was not required while absorption was in progress. The internal supply plus the anion supply adequately supplemented uptake from the atmosphere even for the high respirational level of absorbing roots. When nitrogen was supplied as ammonia, aeration or an adequate heavy metal supplement was required. Apparently these elements catalyze oxygen absorption at low oxygen tension; they increase the efficiency of oxygen utilization; or in some way they stimulate synthetic processes so that the internal supply of oxygen is increased.

Hoagland and Broyer (1936) and Prevot and Steward (1936) have shown that excised root systems having no internal oxygen supply require forced aeration for optimum absorption of salts. Potato root tissues required aeration with an atmosphere containing 10 percent oxygen for maximum absorption (Steward, Berry, and Broyer, 1936). Barley roots used by Hoagland and Broyer were able to accumulate some salt, although the percentage of oxygen was reduced to 5 percent or even less (Hoagland and Broyer, 1936).

Certain plants, notably squash and cotton, respond to forced aeration even when grown on nutrient solutions containing nitrate and microelements. Although cereals may respond to forced aeration by a notable shortening of their roots, this may not be reflected by increased yields. Cereals consequently do not appear to correspond in oxygen requirement with squash and cotton; it may be that because of their structure their internal supply is adequate. Possibly the requirement for aeration may relate to the length and form of intercellular channels of the root. A notable development of the cortical aeration system is found in the roots of many water plants.

The oxygen supply derived from nitrate may be an important source to deeply penetrating roots of some plants, especially during rapid growth in spring. Nitrates leached into the subsoil by winter rains would thus constitute an important factor in root penetration and hence in plant distribution. The presence of reduced sulphur in proteins and of organic compounds of phosphorus in xylem exudate indicates a similar function for these elements (Pierre and Pohlman, 1933).

ION UPTAKE

Although the complex interionic relations of salt uptake affect transport only secondarily through their effects on plant growth, the close parallelism between ion uptake and root exudation has much support (Hoagland, 1936; Hoagland and Broyer, 1936; Laine, 1934; Skoog, Broyer, and Grossenbacher, 1938). Once accumulation by the symplast of the root cortex has been accomplished, the migration to and release within the stele seems almost a foregone conclusion, for the mechanics of the process seem inherent to the structure. The relative abundance of the various ions in the xylem sap is a complex matter of accumulation potentials, mobilities, and ion penetrability. There seems to be little evidence that these affect the end results except as they determine osmotic concentration.

ORGANIC NUTRIENT SUPPLY

Since the ability of roots to accumulate ions depends upon energy from foods, a high rate of ion uptake would necessitate an ample food supply. Esau (1943) has shown that the protophloem sieve tubes in the primary region of the root differentiate much closer to the apex than do the protoxylem elements. Hence an adequate supply of food materials is assured throughout the absorbing region of the root. Radial arrangement of the primary vascular strands assures free movement of foods to the cortex via the symplast without excessive leakage into the xylem.

It has been found that, in the absence of an adequate supply and distribution of foods via the phloem, an external supply via the culture medium is helpful (Prevot and Steward, 1936; White,

1938). The ability to accumulate and distribute carbohydrates commonly attributed to phloem parenchyma may be common to all parenchyma, the supply being more important than the exact specialization of the particular cell system. If this is true, the root pressure mechanism of Münch (1930) is not a workable one.

WATER MOVEMENT

Water absorption by roots may take place under widely differing conditions of pressure. When uptake exceeds transpiration loss, the xylem sap is under positive pressure and water absorption by the root is accomplished with an appreciable expenditure of energy. Under these conditions water movement is relatively slow, taking place along an osmotic gradient between the xylem and the culture medium. Any factor that increases the concentration of solutes in the xylem would accelerate water movement. As Hoagland and Broyer (1936) have shown, rapid exudation accompanies rapid ion absorption.

When transpiration exceeds water uptake, water balance shifts to the negative side and the roots assume a passive role; water absorption is less dependent upon solute absorption. Under all conditions, however, water absorption results from movement along a water activity gradient, transpiration pull tending to reduce the activity of water in the xylem even more effectively than do the solutes that are released by root cells. Solute uptake, on the other hand, depends upon solute supply and an activity gradient of metabolism and is influenced by water movement only as the latter presents more ions at the absorbing surfaces or reduced concentration of ions in the stele, or accelerates the movement of gases through the root tissues. Hoagland and Broyer (1936) and Freeland (1935) have indicated that the maintenance of the supply of salts will increase salt absorption by roots.

Absorption of salts and water are visualized as being independent according to the above scheme. There seems to be no reason, however, for assuming, with Curtis (1935), that a partition of mineral nutrients takes place between xylem and phloem in the root. The presence of both organic and inorganic nitrogen compounds in the xylem sap, as well as other mineral nutrients (Anderson, 1929; Hoagland and Broyer, 1936; Pierre and Pohlman, 1933), indicates that these materials move en masse in the transpiration stream; the relative abundance of either seems related to the conditions that exist in the functioning roots at the time of absorption.

SECONDARY MOVEMENT OF SOLUTES

The relation of primary to secondary movement of materials in vascular tissues depends upon the relative activities of the functioning tissues. For example, organic radicals utilized in nitrate reduction in the roots depend upon the relation of available sugars to nitrate absorbed (Leonard, 1936). In trees where absorption and movement are relatively slow, most of the translocated nitrogen is in organic combination (Thomas, 1927). Lack of oxygen in the atmosphere surrounding the roots of trees may be another factor in this phenomenon. Nitrogen when absorbed as nitrate by shallow-rooted herbs may be largely moved as such. This occurs in tomato when copiously fertilized with nitrate. It also occurs in the case of weeds growing in corrals and even in open pastures, occasionally causing nitrate poisoning in cattle. In other plants—cotton (Mason and Maskell, 1931) and sunflower (Leonard, 1936), for example—both nitrates and reduced nitrogen compounds move in the transpiration stream. The fate of nitrogen compounds depends ultimately upon the ability of the shoot to retain them. If this is low, they may enter the assimilate stream and again migrate into the roots (Maskell and Mason, 1929a). In the long-time economy of plants this problem is unimportant; the primary shoot meristems and vascular cambium are the principal tissues that utilize such compounds. At senescence the proteins of leaves may be remobilized and moved into the stems for over-winter storage.

GENERAL ASPECTS OF THE POSTULATED MECHANISM

The process of salt migration in roots seems definitely associated with the process of accumulation by root cells; the ultimate release of solutes into the dead xylem vessels involves, in addition, a process that may, for lack of a better name, be termed secretion. Some physiologists have attempted to identify this activity with differential accumulative capacity at the outer and inner sides of individual root cells. Some have related it with electrical gradients within the root. It is difficult, however, to determine the cause-and-effect relations of electrical phenomena in a root containing demonstrated concentration gradients of electrolytes.

It is proposed here that the structural relations of the root impose upon the tissues certain environmental conditions that enable the external tissues to accumulate solutes while the internal tissues lose them. The actual movement of solutes from cell to cell within the root is assumed to occur by diffusion, accelerated by protoplasmic streaming, except along plasmodesmata where streaming has not been demonstrated.

Observed rates of uptake and exudation seem compatible with this mechanism. The presence of bromide ion in xylem exudate of squash within 30 minutes after exposure of the roots to a solution having 800 ppm KBr indicates one measured rate. Assuming streaming at 2.0 cm per hour (Crafts, 1933) and a distance of 0.5 mm to be traversed from root hair to xylem, 1½ minutes would be consumed in carrying the ions through the lumina of the living cells or about 99 percent of the required distance. With upward flow at 1 cm per minute another 10 minutes would be required to move them to the ends of the open vessels. This would leave 18½ minutes for diffusion of the ions through the .005 mm of protoplasm traversed along the plasmodesmata. This seems possible in terms of the concentrations involved.

chapter five

Mechanism of Accumulation and Water Movement

MECHANISM OF ACCUMULATION

Many attempts have been made to visualize the mechanism by which cells accumulate ions. These include exchange, in which H^+ and HCO_3^- produced within cells are supposed to exchange for ions in the culture medium. This cannot be entirely discarded as a theory, because of demonstrated replacement of NO_3^- ions by HCO_3^- ions. However, many aspects of ion accumulation cannot be reconciled with a mechanism dependent entirely upon exchange phenomena.

Other mechanisms include adsorption of ions on colloids inside the cells, differential hydration, and Donnan equilibria. Hoagland was able to refute these various theories and to prove that accumulation is an active process requiring oxygen and organic assimilates and a favorable temperature. He was able to show that with high-salt plants there may be a fair correlation between transpiration and salt absorption but with low-salt plants such correlation fails completely (Hoagland, 1937).

Hoagland proved that permeability per se did not offer an answer to ion accumulation. Cells that would not accumulate KBr when bubbled with pure nitrogen took up the salt actively when bubbling was done with oxygen. Continuing his investigations with plants growing both in soil and in water cultures he studied the factors determining the availability of ions to roots, the environmental factors favoring maximum uptake of ions, movement of ions inside the plant, and the role of various elements in plant growth. Much of this research is described in his book *Inorganic Plant Nutrition* (Hoagland, 1944).

The availability of ions to plants is greatly affected by soil properties, particularly the quantity and quality of colloids present. The clay fraction of the soil is known to hold cations against the leaching effect of moving water, and yet plants can absorb these cations. According to the soil-solution theory of plant feeding, an exchange of hydrogen ions for nutrient cations takes place via the intervening water layers.

Jenny and Overstreet (1939), using radioactive elements, made studies with roots in colloid suspensions that convinced them that exchange of ions may take place through direct contact of root cell walls with soil colloids, with no free solution involved. Much experimental evidence has been presented to support this idea (Jenny, 1951).

In view of the polyuronide nature of the pectic fraction of root cell walls it seems logical that such an exchange may take place. This mechanism explains uptake of certain elements from soils in which the concentration in soil extracts may be exceedingly low.

The contact-exchange theory of ion uptake involves a mechanism making possible reactions between adsorbents without the participation of free electrolytes (Jenny, 1951). This theory rests on the concept of ion redistribution within intermingling electric double layers. Although presence of water is not necessary to contact exchange, this process may proceed in the presence of water and it may be reversible. Symbolically, the relationship of contact uptake and contact depletion may be depicted as follows:

$$\overset{R}{\bigtriangledown}\ \mathrm{H} + \mathrm{K}\ \boxed{\text{clay}} = \overset{R}{\bigtriangledown}\ \mathrm{K} + \mathrm{H}\ \boxed{\text{clay}}$$

$$\overset{R}{\bigtriangledown} = \text{roots and } \boxed{\text{clay}} = \text{clay particles}$$

The direction of the reaction will depend upon the relative amounts of the two absorbents and on the forces with which the ions are held to the two surfaces.

It should be pointed out that the contact-exchange mechanism explains only the interchange between the clay fraction of the soil and the adsorbent phase of the plant root, presumably the polyuronide fraction of the cell wall pectin. Uptake by the symplast from this phase of the apoplast involves some other mechanism. Furthermore, the contact-exchange concept as proposed by Jenny and his associates offers no explanation for uptake of anions.

Lundegardh (1950) as a result of years of research on salt uptake and xylem exudation by roots has proposed that the motive power of salt accumulation and active salt transport from cell to cell is anion respiration involving a cytochrome-cytochrome oxidase system. He builds his concept of salt absorption on a number of properties of the root. For example, he starts with the premise that the protoplasmic membrane concerned with ion absorption is built of oriented molecules, some of which are dissociated on the acid side so that loosely bound H ions are associated with the surface. By dissociation the membrane thus attains a residual negative charge.

In addition Lundegardh postulates that the surface of the root possesses positive adsorption sites that, in the absence of anions of acids, are saturated with OH^- and possibly a few HCO_3^- ions. In normal nutrient solutions he pictures the wheat root as occupied by large quantities of metallic cations, a much smaller amount of H^+ ions, and minute amounts of OH^- ions and ions of neutral salts. The first stage of absorption he considers to be the interchange of cations and anions at the surface of the protoplasm. The conditions for the absorption of cations and anions from the culture medium are fundamentally different. Whereas metallic cations always move from dilute solution in the direction of the potential gradient—that is, into the surface phase—anions are repelled from the negative surface and an extra supply of energy is needed to overcome the resistance. This extra supply of energy, Lundegardh postulates, is provided by anion respiration, a process correlated with anion accumulation, that is superposed on the fundamental respiration required for other life processes. Lundegardh distinguishes between the processes of adsorption on the surface of the symplast, passage of solutes into the body of the cytoplasm, and release into the conduits of the xylem. The active absorption of salts he considers to be the up-hill process, the exudation of salts the down-hill process. The motive power is the anion respiration.

According to the anion respiration theory anions move in the opposite direction to that of electrons taken over by the cytochrome system from a hydrogen donor and transferred through the different cytochromes and cytochrome oxidase to the molecular oxygen. The

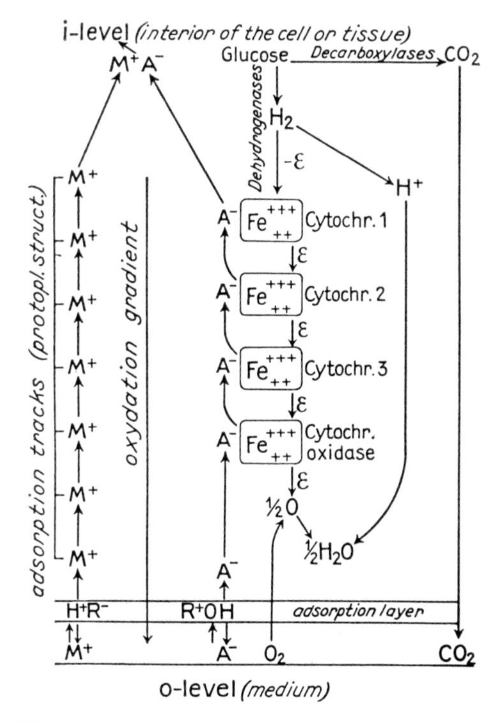

Fig. 5-1. Diagrammatic representation of the theory of anion respiration. (From Lundegardh, 1950)

ionized oxygen then reacts with hydrogen ions to form water. This is the main energy-liberating process. It is illustrated in the diagram of Fig. 5-1 (Lundegardh, 1950).

Hoagland and Steward (1939) have criticized Lundegardh's concept of anion respiration. While agreeing that salt uptake is coupled with aerobic respiration, they look on salt respiration—that is, the increased activity associated with active salt accumulation—as an unspecific metabolic activity.

As research on ion uptake by roots progressed, the process was analyzed in greater and greater detail. In 1947 Jacobson and Overstreet introduced the concept of a carrier to explain potassium absorption by barley roots (see also Lundegardh, 1950). According to this idea the absorption of a cation may be expressed as follows:

$$M^+ + HR = MR + H^+$$

and that of an anion as

$$A^- + R'OH = R'A + OH^-$$

where HR is the metabolically produced cation (Jacobson *et al.*, 1950; Overstreet, Jacobson, and Handley, 1952) binding compound and R'OH the equivalent anion binding compound. This expression of the relation between the absorbed cation and the carrier is in somewhat the same terms as those used by biochemists to explain the enzyme-substrate complex.

Jacobson (1955), reflecting the long period of ion absorption study in the Division of Plant Nutrition at Berkeley, states, "When ions are absorbed from the external solution, equivalent amounts of other ions are liberated into the solution by the roots. These ions are primarily H^+ and OH^- (or HCO_3^-) which become available in ionic form during the absorption reaction. Unequal absorption of cations and anions by plant roots is reflected in gains or losses of inorganic ions and changes in organic acid content of the roots." Knowing that barley roots are capable of fixing small amounts of CO_2 (Overstreet *et al.*, 1940), Jacobson went on to show that radioactive CO_2 ($C^{14}O_2$) was fixed in excised barley roots and that the principal constituent among the labeled compounds found was malic acid. $C^{14}O_2$ was fixed from $K_2C^{14}O_3$ solution both with and without KBr, Br being taken up at the same time as $C^{14}O_2$ in the former situation. From KH_2PO_4 solution, $C^{14}O_2$ was more actively absorbed and more maleate was formed than from $K_2C^{14}O_3$ and KBr alone. Less $C^{14}O_2$ was fixed from $K_2C^{14}O_3$ to which $CaBr_2$ was added.

Lundegardh (1955), developing the carrier hypothesis, speaks of "specific carriers" for specific ions and mentions that nucleic acids form nucleates with different cations having specific solubilities. He develops a series of schemes for diagraming ion uptake. His first scheme indicates the role of carriers in the absorption, translocation, and accumulation of ions into the interior of the cell. It explains continuous ion import as owing to either continuous extension of the exchange capacity or a continuous production of organic acids. True accumulation, he recognizes, requires special features involving expenditure of metabolic energy. Lundegardh mentions his claim that anions are actively transported and that cations are passively dragged along into the cell by carriers. He mentions also the possible role of phosphorylation-dephosphorylation in glucose accumulation but returns to anion respiration to bring his final scheme into focus. He describes his scheme as "structurally guided electrophoresis" and proposes that under appropriate structural conditions it can constitute an effective pump. In this scheme Lundegardh combines the mechanism diagramed in Fig. 5-1 with a cation carrier *MR* to cover accumulation of neutral salts.

In order to reconcile the mechanisms of cellular accumulation of ions with the exudation of xylem sap by excised roots at concentrations above that of the culture medium, Lundegardh proposes that the cytochrome system (anion respiration) of each cell of the root tissue not only pumps salts into the vacuole but also lifts the salt concentration in the "free space" to a level exceeding that of the surrounding medium.

The term "apparent free space" (AFS) has been introduced (Hope and Stevens, 1952) to designate that portion of the plant cell readily accessible to ions by diffusion. Epstein (1955) terms this "outer space." Contrasting with this outer or free space is "inner" or "osmotic space," from which ions may not readily diffuse. Uptake of ions by outer or free space is considered to be passive and reversible; uptake by inner or osmotic space is active and irreversible.

AFS as used by Hope and Stevens (1952) and Briggs and Robertson (1957) involves not only the region freely accessible by diffusion but also regions in which ions are restrained by labile binding sites, accessible by exchange. Their free space is the same as Epstein's outer space; their osmotic volume is equivalent to Epstein's inner space.

The free-space concept has been used by a number of investigators (Hope and Stevens, 1952; Hope, 1953; Butler, 1953a, b; Hope and Robertson, 1953; Hylmö, 1953, 1955; Epstein, 1955, 1956; Lundegardh, 1955; Briggs and Robertson, 1957; Jacobson *et al.*, 1957; Levitt, 1957; Eppley and Blinks, 1957), and others. Values for AFS range from 7.8 percent in pea (Hylmö, 1953) to 33 percent in wheat (Butler, 1955) and 45.3 percent for *Porphyra* (Eppley and

Blinks, 1957). Jacobson *et al.* (1957), studying uptake of K^+ and Br^- from KBr solutions, found the amounts removed from root tissues by water to agree approximately with values reported by others. However, when they corrected their absorption data for these loosely held ions they found the corrections to be minor and to have a negligible effect on their absorption curves except under conditions of relatively low uptake; that is, when the concentration of absorbed ions in the tissues was of the same magnitude as, or less than, that in the external solution.

Levitt (1957) makes several pertinent suggestions with regard to the various estimates of the volume of free space. Correcting for hydration of the cellulose and pectins known to make up the cell walls of absorbing root cells, he arrives at values of around 10 to 12 percent rather than the 3 percent or less that others have calculated for cell-wall volume. AFS would be about $\frac{7}{10}$ of this or 7.7 to 8.4 percent.

Concerning the values of AFS of 20 to 33 percent that have been quoted by Butler (1955) and Epstein (1955), Levitt proposes that water films of a thickness of 0.02 mm that they failed to remove could account for these high values. Correcting for films of this thickness, Levitt arrives again at values in the neighborhood of 8 percent for AFS. This he concludes represents the space in the walls available for free diffusion.

The importance of free-space measurements is pointed up by the assumption of many workers that free space occupies too large a volume to reside in the cell walls and hence that the outer part, or perhaps most of the cytoplasm, of cells is included. Levitt objects to this assumption on the basis of the known evidence for the semipermeable nature of the external plasma membrane. Crafts and Yamaguchi (1960) have objected to the assumption on the basis that it would eliminate the plasmodesmata from the transport mechanism proposed by Crafts and Boyer (1938). If the free space of the absorbing cell is identical with the medium of the cell wall accessible by free diffusion, then the concepts of uptake via the apoplast and transport along the symplast (Münch, 1930) would seem to be useful (Crafts and Broyer, 1938; Arisz, 1956).

Lundegardh's (1955) statement that exudation through the vascular epithelium (xylem exudation) supports the conclusion that the actual salt concentration in the free space is higher than the concentration in the nutrient medium is a rationalization that overlooks not only the definition of free space but also the obvious characteristics of salt accumulation. If the function of the anion respiration is to pump salts into the vacuole only to have them leak passively back to the free space and thence to the external medium (Lundegardh's scheme G), it is difficult to understand the rapid transport of Br^- found by Hoagland and Broyer (1936), the exudation of the volume of sap found by Crafts and Broyer (1938), and the fact found many times that K^+ absorbed by cells cannot be entirely removed by leaching.

Likewise, the assumption of Kramer (1957) that all of the cytoplasm external to the tonoplast resides in free space, and that the sieve tubes of the phloem also partake of the nature of free space, seems to be an overgeneralization. Kramer does not agree with Lundegardh that the free-space concept can be reconciled with the exudation from the xylem of sap, higher in concentration than the culture medium. He states "At present there seems to be no satisfactory way of explaining salt accumulation in the xylem." He abandons the Crafts-Broyer theory as being inoperative "if ions can diffuse in and out of the cytoplasm, as must be the case if cytoplasm is included in outer space." Kramer (1957) would minimize the role of the endodermis, with its suberized Casparian strip, in root function. However, to the writer it seems that, without this barrier to leakage, the commonly observed root pressure that often attains values up to 2 atmospheres (see also White, 1938b) would not be found. The suberized primary endodermis is always present in absorbing roots in the region of root hairs where uptake of water and salts is most active. In more mature regions where the endodermis is disrupted the xylem becomes limited by the vascular cambium, an active layer capable of retaining solution under pressure. Hylmö (1953) similarly considers that the bulk of the cytoplasm is in free space and that the transpiration stream draws solute from the culture medium through the shoot. He considers that the medium is drawn passively through cell walls and cytoplasm but that ions cannot passively penetrate the vacuoles. He grants that if the concept of mass flow is correct, every cell in the plant accumulates ions individually from the surrounding cell-wall and cytoplasm solution (free space) by a process analogous to salt uptake by unicellular algae. Such a view would visualize the root as being like a polythene bag full of yeast cells. In so doing, it discounts over 100 years of work by plant anatomists on the structural relations of roots and it fails completely to explain the active pumping of xylem sap reported by Crafts and Broyer (1938) and many others.

In a later paper Kylin and Hylmö (1957) recognize two different processes in the uptake and transport of sulfur to the aerial parts of wheat plants. At low external concentrations an active "metabolic" process predominates; at high concentrations of the culture medium the passive process is dominant.

Broyer (1956) presents data on barley root experiments where uptake periods were followed by analyses of washed and unwashed roots. In the case of low-salt high-sugar roots the amounts of salt lost upon washing were insignificant whereas washing removed very significant quantities of salts from the high-salts roots. AFS values varied from low to about 20 percent of the total root volume. This value is probably subject to the criticism of Levitt (1957) with respect to retention of a film even after centrifuging.

Russell and Shorrocks (1957) controvert the conclusion of Hylmö concerning the passivity of salt movement in the transpiration stream. They point to two reasons for the popular acceptance of this concept: (1) the close correlation shown in certain experiments between the rate of transpiration and the rate of transport of salt to plant shoots; and (2) the evidence that the outer surface of the cytoplasm of cells does not present a high resistance to entrance of salts—that is, the concept of apparent free space. They point out on the other hand the large body of evidence indicating the independence of salt uptake and water movement, and the dependence of salt uptake upon metabolic activity.

Russell and Shorrocks point out that the concomitant uptake of water and salts by the pea roots used by Hylmö follows from their nutrient status and parallels results of Hoagland and Broyer. Studying phosphorus and rubidium uptake by young barley plants grown at differing nutrient levels, and using shade to reduce transpiration, they proved the independence of salt and water uptake. Calculating a factor

$$\text{T.S.C.F.} = \frac{\text{concentration of ions in transpiration stream}}{\text{concentration of ions in external medium}}$$

they obtained the results diagramed in Fig. 5-2.

From this experiment and a number of others, some of which involved rubidium, Russell and Shorrocks concluded that the extent to which the transfer of both phosphate and rubidium to plant shoots is affected by transpiration rate depends on both the salt status of the plant and the concentration of the external medium. When the initial phosphate status of the plants was low and dilute external concentrations were used, the content of the shoots was practically independent of transpiration. When either the concen-

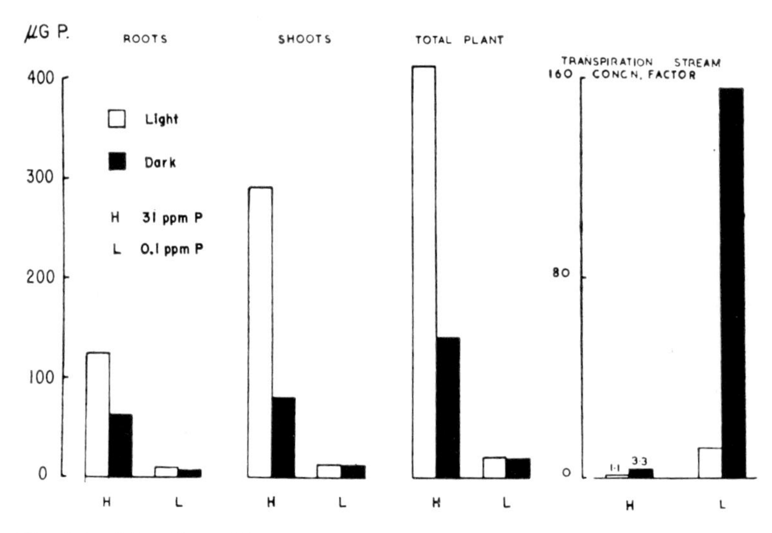

Fig. 5-2. The effect of shading on the absorption and distribution of phosphate and on the "transpiration stream concentration factor." Duration of treatment, 24 hours. (From Russell and Shorrocks, 1957)

tration of phosphate in the culture medium or the phosphate status of the plants was high, a closer correlation between shoot content and transpiration obtained.

Experiments with rubidium showed less variation between shoot content and transpiration over a comparable range in external concentrations; the transport of rubidium to the shoots was never independent of transpiration down to the lowest concentration of rubidium employed. The effect of increased transpiration, however, was greatest at high concentrations.

The conclusion of Russell and Shorrocks was that the overall process whereby ions are transferred from the external medium across the root to the stele and up into the shoots is not controlled by transpiration. One step in this process that may be rate limiting in plants of high salt status is influenced by transpiration. They question the dependence upon transpiration of the step involving transfer of ions from the culture medium across the cortex to the stele. The relationship between salt uptake and metabolism has been well established by Hoagland, Steward, Broyer, Lundegardh, and others. Respiratory inhibitors have been shown to reduce both the absorption and transport of ions to plant shoots.

When transpiration is low and the ion supply small, the concentration in the vascular sap may exceed that of the culture medium by a factor of over 100. When the external concentration is high and transpiration is rapid, this factor may be less than unity. The high concentration gradient against which ions are transported is evidence for an active process requiring energy. Furthermore, the large concentration and pressure gradients between the external medium and the xylem sap of slowly transpiring plants precludes the possibility of pathways for passive diffusion across the root. There is conclusive evidence for a high resistance barrier—possibly the endodermis—across which ions are actively moved in the intact root. This view does not dispute the existence in the cortex of a cell-wall phase freely accessible to ions.

Broyer (1956) comes to conclusions very similar to those of Russell and Shorrocks and he goes on to discuss the mechanism of salt accumulation. Considering the effect of various inhibitors of respiration, he provides data indicating that although the respiratory level under anaerobic or cyanide treatment is higher than at low temperatures with aeration, accumulation is favored by the latter. He cites evidence that the energy supply provided by respiration is greater than that needed to account for accumulation but he finds no means for distinguishing between salt respiration and fundamental respiration.

Broyer submits a schematic diagram (Fig. 5-3) for indicating the nature of the processes of movement of materials across the protoplasm. Providing for the external surface, the bulk interior, and the internal interface of the cytoplasm, this scheme comes nearer than many previously proposed to explaining solute uptake in terms of the complexity of the system that has been recognized for years by plant anatomists and cytologists.

Broyer considers that the physiological thickness of the ectoplasm and endoplasm may vary inversely through processes determined in part by environmental factors and that the mesoplasm is of indefinite and possibly inconsequential thickness. In later

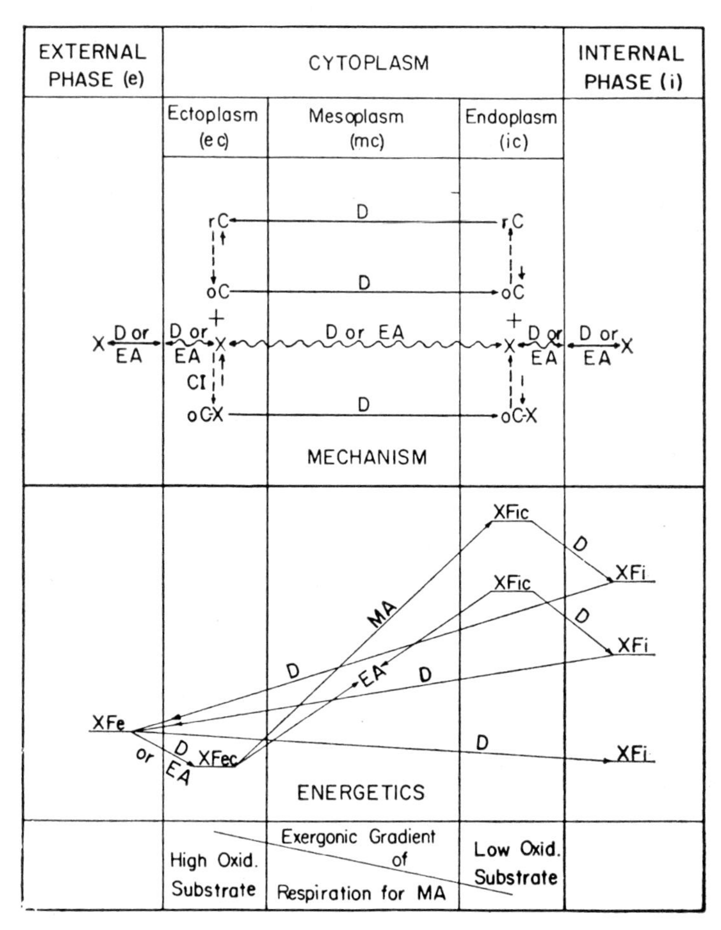

Fig. 5-3. Schematic, generalized diagram of the nature of the processes of movement of materials across protoplasm interposed in a two-phased system. (From Broyer, 1956.) X = a component material capable of migration; e, i, ec, ic, mc = subscripts indicating location. oC = oxidized cytoplasmic constituents concerned in unidirectional translocation of material X. rC = reduced cytoplasmic constituents. XF = specific free energy (energy intensity) of component. D = diffusion. EA = exchange adsorption. MA = metabolic accumulation. CI = cytoplasmic interaction between oC and X. In upper part of figure, arrow with solid shaft = migration, where permeability is relatively high; with wavy shaft, where relatively low. Arrow with dashed shaft = chemical reaction. In lower part of figure, arrow with solid shaft = energy changes of X.

discussion of the properties of the cytoplasm in absorbing cells and sieve tubes it will be pointed out that the mesoplasm may provide an important channel for quite rapid transport of solutes.

WATER MOVEMENT

Few studies have been made during the past few decades on water transport in plants. Several, however, have added to our knowledge of this process. Van den Honert (1948) has pointed out that the overall transport may be considered as a catenary process; that is, one made up of a number of interlinked steps. When movement resulting from transpiration is in a steady state, the same quantity of water per unit of time passes through the living root cells, the xylem conduits, the living leaf cells, the intercellular spaces of the leaf, and the stomatal openings. Through each part the transport is governed by a potential difference at either extremity and a resistance between these.

Proceeding with an analysis of these individual steps, van den Honert points out that the successive transport of water in the plant is a catenary process and that the overall rate of movement depends on which part meets the highest resistance. This, according to his analysis, is the process that takes place in the vapor phase—that is, the diffusion of water molecules from the mesophyll cell walls through the stomata into the outer atmosphere. This is the part over which the plant has the greatest control through stomatal movement.

Even more recently Philip (1958) has proposed that during even moderate transpiration, removal of water from the soil by roots results in a large moisture gradient close to the root surface. As a result, much of the water absorbed by roots may be taken up as vapor. Thus as a soil approaches permanent wilting percentage, water uptake by roots may take place by distillation, and soil temperature as well as the availability of moisture becomes important.

This vapor phase is undoubtedly a barrier to salt uptake; it probably also presents a resistance to movement. Interestingly the plant, by cuticle development, by stomatal closure, by adapting to moisture stress through changes in the osmotic concentration of solutes, and by limiting growth, can survive such stress if it is not prolonged. During this time it maintains an internal atmosphere with a relative humidity approaching saturation.

Work by Scholander and associates (1955, 1957) and Greenidge (1954, 1955a, b) has indicated that the water in plants constitutes a continuum, that it continues to move through the xylem in the presence of gas in many of the conduits, and that the severance of all continuous water columns by overlapping cuts still allows enough movement to maintain a healthy top, provided soil moisture is adequate and transpiration is not high. Evidently the intermicellar channels in the xylem walls are sufficient to handle a moderate flow of water; xylem conduits seem to have end walls of sufficiently closed nature to prevent the unlimited expansion of water vapor; and the xylem of liannas has enough tracheids, fibers, and walls to provide adequate conduction even when the larger vessels are filled with air. These air-filled conduits may become refilled with water by capillarity during times of low water stress. The pressure of opposed menisci is sufficient to cause the air bubbles to dissolve if given time. Many of these vessels are refilled during the winter when water soaks into the branches and trunk via leaf scars, wounds, and so forth; many remain air filled and are replaced by new wood laid down by cambial activity.

DISCUSSION: MOVEMENT OF WATER AND SALTS

In concluding this portion of the subject it will be of interest to analyze in some detail the overall process of water and salt movement in plants. Many of the early studies on this phase of plant physiology were approached with an oversimplified view. Movement of water and uptake and movement of salts are undoubtedly both catenary processes that are virtually independent, though at times and under some circumstances they seem interdependent.

From the standpoint of the cytology of cells and the anatomy of plants it should be evident that the very structures that make up the media for movement are complex. Starting from the soil or the culture solution the first of these structures are the walls of the epidermis of the root. These consist of three phases: (1) the cellulose micelles, which, from investigators' experience with chromatography, are known to have weak binding sites; (2) the pectin matrix with its polyuronides that constitute an exchange medium with fairly strong adsorption spots; (3) the aqueous phase comprised of water having varying degrees of randomness, depending on its association with the cellulose, the pectins, and their adsorbed ions.

All of the water in the aqueous phase of the cell wall is probably somewhat ordered—much of it in close proximity to the micelles of the cellulose framework and the pectic gel is undoubtedly highly ordered. It is proposed, from the analysis given in this chapter, that the evidence points to this aqueous phase of the cell wall as the true free space of the plant body.

Next to be considered is the protoplast of the cell. This may be subdivided into at least four phases; cytologists would insist on more.

(1) **The ectoplast,** in itself a complex structure. This phase can be seen under the microscope, especially if the cell is plasmolyzed, under which condition myriads of small projections may occasionally be seen attaching it to the wall. This structure is undoubtedly a membrane; it has been shown to contain many enzymes; its lipoprotein mosaic nature indicates the presence of many and diverse binding sites; it constitutes the surface of most intimate contact of the plant with its terrestrial environment.

(2) **The mesoplasm,** the body of the cytoplasm that forms the matrix for the activities of the nucleus, the plastids, the mitochondria, and the microsomes. The main movements of protoplasmic streaming take place in the mesoplasm. This activity has been enlisted to explain rapid translocation of solutes from end to end of the single cell. Because of its constant high activity and constant mixing it seems impossible that the mesoplasm itself can constitute a membrane.

(3) **The endoplast,** or tonoplast, the limiting layer separating the mesoplasm from the vacuole. It has long been postulated that the endoplast is the principal differentially permeable membrane of the plant cell. It is known that certain vital dyes can be localized in the mesoplasm and not pass the endoplast into the vacuole; others can pass the whole cytoplasmic layer and concentrate in the vacuole (neutral red). Sugars are known to pass the endoplast slowly and with difficulty. Brooks (1938a, b, 1943a) found that radioactive KCl entered the protoplasm of the cell rapidly and built up to a concentration above that of the external medium and of the vacuole. Broyer (1950) showed that anions absorbed from culture solution may migrate through the protoplasm to the xylem without accumulating in the vacuoles. Arisz (1954) found similar effects with salt

in *Vallisneria.* These findings would seem to indicate that the endoplasm constitutes a membrane of special properties.

(4) **The vacuole.** This is filled primarily with aqueous solution but may contain ergastic substances such as tannins, protein bodies, fat globules, and crystals. Peculiar starch grains and extruded nucleoli may be found in the lumina of sieve tubes (Esau, 1953). Although the early studies of Hoagland and Davis (1923) showed that the vacuolar sap was highly concentrated in ions, much subsequent work indicates that the vacuole may serve simply as a storage organ and not as the main region of accumulation. The assumption of Epstein (1956) that solutes moving across the cortex of the root must necessarily pass successively through cell wall, cytoplasm, vacuole, cytoplasm, cell wall, etc., seems unnecessary in view of evidence for symplastic movement within the cytoplasm. In a recent paper Epstein (1960) has accepted the symplast concept.

Another cell constituent that may prove to be of extreme importance is the endoplasmic reticulum. Known for some time in animal cells, this structure has recently been described and illustrated in plant cells in great detail (Whaley *et al.,* 1959, 1960; Shalla, 1960). According to electron microscope photomicrographs it is apparently made up of a fine double layer of dense material that ramifies through the mesoplasm, contacts the nucleus, passes from cell to cell via the plasmodesmata, and is in intimate association with both the endoplast and the ectoplast. It appears to have many of the properties of the ectoplastic membrane yet it is present throughout the plasma of the cell. If, as seems possible, this reticulum constitutes an active membranelike phase, it may bear the principal binding sites that are involved in solute uptake by living cells. Since it invades the mesoplasm, contacts the nucleus and endoplast, and must be in constant flux in the streaming protoplasm, it may well constitute the mechanism responsible for absorption and transport of ions by the symplast. Conceivably it may combine the properties of an active membrane with the essential features of the postulated carrier system.

A phase of the plant cell that has been sorely neglected is the cell wall-cytoplasm interface (CWCI). Here meet the three phases described for the cell wall and the important ectoplast of the cytoplasm. Here the two adsorptive phases of the cell wall, the cellulose and pectin, meet and form a continuum with the complex of binding sites of the lipoprotein mosaic of the protoplast. If carriers are involved in the absorption of ions, here they absorb from the passive cell-wall phases and start the up-hill process of accumulation.

Recent work on the uptake of labeled organic compounds by roots (Crafts and Yamaguchi, 1960) indicates that some compounds are rapidly adsorbed by roots, passed on into the stele, and then transported to the tops—for example, 2,2-dichloropropionate (dalapon), 3-*p*-chlorophenyl-1,1-dimethylurea (monuron), and 2-chloro-4,6-bis(ethyl-amino)-*s*-triazine (simazin); others, however, are rapidly adsorbed and held without transfer to the tops—for example, 2,4-dichlorophenoxyacetate (2,4-D) and indole acetic acid (IAA). It is proposed that all are adsorbed at the CWCI: the first three are able to move on through the ectoplast and translocate via the mesoplasm from cell to cell (symplastic movement) to the stele where they are released, but the latter two, being unable to traverse the ectoplast, remain concentrated at the interface.

Brooks (1943a, b) has reported on the rapid intake and later loss of ions from animal cells. Clor (1951) found that 2,4-D, applied to a leaf of a cotton plant growing in culture solution with a second plant, leaks into the culture medium and is absorbed by the second plant with the production of typical 2,4-D symptoms. This finding has been confirmed with C^{14}-labeled 2,4-D by counting of the culture solution and autoradiographing the receptor plant. Preston *et al.* (1954) reported transfer of α-methoxyphenylacetic acid from one plant to another through their root systems (see also Linder *et al.*, 1957) and Linder *et al.* (1958) have reported similar behavior of 2,3,6-trichlorobenzoic acid. Blackman (1955) has found that 2,4-D is rapidly absorbed by roots of *Lemna minor* and *Salvinia natans* and soon lost back into the culture solution. Later he found a similar response on the part of sunflower and sorghum (Blackman, 1957). Recent work (Crafts and Yamaguchi, current studies) has shown that 2,4-D absorbed by barley root segments may be largely washed out by repeated rinsing with the straight culture solution. In all of these cases a certain amount of the 2,4-D was retained but the major part was lost from the treated roots.

The ease with which the absorption process is reversed in these cases would seem to indicate that most of the 2,4-D had not entered the living cell but was retained on an exchange medium that may be under the influence of the living cell. This would seem to indicate the CWCI as the site for a dynamic and reversible type of binding of ions.

The foregoing discussion brings into sharp relief the whole concept of free space. It seems probable, as Levitt has pointed out, that the true free space of the root resides in the aqueous phase of the cell wall. The AFS, on the other hand, involves the true free space plus the adsorption complex of the cell-wall solid phase plus the CWCI including the dynamic exchange surface of the ectoplast. If the latter is under the influence of the living cytoplasm, and may reversibly bind and release ions, it seems that the observed loss of ions considered as free-space diffusion may in fact be a combination of true free-space diffusion and a fortuitous release of ions from the ectoplast, a process that at present is entirely unpredictable. If this is true, one may question the true significance of the factors of time, concentration, aeration, pretreatment, and so on, that enter into free-space measurements. Since a number of plants transport 2,4-D to their tops in differing quantities, and since one plant species (barley) is able to discriminate between 2,4-D and dalapon, retaining the former in the roots and freely transporting the latter to the tops, it seems that plants exert a definite protoplasmic control over root absorption. The early demonstration of widely differing concentration factors between sodium and potassium accumulation indicate the same ability. This does not fit the views of Hylmö (1953) and Kramer (1957) regarding the passive uptake and movement of solutes in the transpiration stream.

The many studies on root function made with root segments and excised root systems completely immersed in the culture medium have a common weakness in that they fail to measure root pumping. Any work involving energetics of absorption must necessarily contain errors if such material is used, because the pumping is an active, energy-consuming process. Another common weakness of root-function work is the failure to consider root growth. This is an important factor, in fact a dominant factor in the growth of a crop during its grand period of nutrient uptake from the soil. Not only are growing plant roots constantly exploring new soil sites; in the growth process there is a constant expansion of the cell wall and the CWCI that provides exchange areas saturated principally by hydrogen and free for exchange with soil cations, or by nitrogen compounds that can adsorb anions. Lundegardh (1950) proposed that the cation binding sites of the root greatly outnumbered the anion binding sites, and Jacobson (1955) claims that when ions are absorbed from the external medium, equivalent amounts of other ions are liberated. These two concepts seem at odds. There seem to be no carefully conducted tests to prove that such equivalent exchange is actually carried out. If the released ions were H^+ and OH^- they would certainly combine at their earliest opportunity to form water and join the inward moving stream through the plant. If they were H^+ and HCO_3^- presumably CO_2 would be released into the soil for eventual loss to the atmosphere and uptake by the leaves so that a CO_2 circuit would be established.

In many of his publications Hoagland claimed that cations and anions are taken up simultaneously by plant roots (see also Brooks, 1938a). If salt absorption is a catenary process there seems to be no reason for stressing the exchange aspect, because ions released into the xylem could be replaced by ions absorbed by the roots along a continuous chain in the symplasm and the cell walls. The almost universal impression that ion uptake by roots takes place by equivalent exchange with the culture medium probably results from the use of root segments and excised roots where the catenary aspect of movement to the shoot is eliminated.

Although the early work with *Valonia* and *Nitella* seems to indicate that plant cells exercise a great discrimination in their uptake of ions from the culture medium, more recent experiments with unbalanced culture solutions and toxic substances such as herbicides show that plants have little power to reject the solutes that are present in their surroundings. Arsenic, borax, chlorate, dalapon, monuron, simazin, IPC, and a host of other compounds are absorbed by plant roots; if absorbed in sufficient quantity, they result in the death of the plants. The older toxicants, such as arsenic, borax, sodium chlorate, and carbon disulfide, were required in quite large quantities to effect complete plant destruction. The substituted ureas and symmetrical triazines are required in only minute amounts (fractions of a part per million) in the soil solution in order to kill plants. Though unable to enter the phloem of plant leaves (Haun and Peterson, 1954; Crafts, 1959; Sheets, 1959), these compounds readily enter roots (Crafts and Yamaguchi, 1960), move up in the transpiration stream (Minshall, 1954), prevent the uptake of CO_2 and the photolysis of water (Cooke, 1956), and kill the plant. Many of these labeled compounds can be used in such minute amounts as tracers that their toxic properties are not expressed, at least in the early stages of an experiment. Hence they may be used as translocation indicators.

With the discovery of systemic chemotherapeutant chemicals a whole new group of agents has been added to the above-mentioned indicators. Dimond and Horsfall (1959) in America and Crowdy and associates (Crowdy and Pramer, 1955; Crowdy, 1959) in Britain have published on this work. It has been shown that sulfonamides, antibiotics, and a host of chemotherapeutants may be absorbed from the culture medium by plant roots and translocated throughout the plant via the transpiration stream. Analysis of the experimental work indicates that these compounds move rapidly and reversibly into cell walls, that they enter the plant root cell by a slower, nonreversible process, and that they may concomitantly or subsequently pass into the stele and ascend to the top of the plant in the transpiration stream through the xylem conduits. Neutral, acidic or basic compounds may be absorbed and translocated. Some may move through the plant unchanged; others may gain or lose in therapeutant activity after absorption (Crowdy *et al.*, 1959a, 1959b). Other findings are that certain minimum water solubility is required for adequate penetration; that increasing lipoid solubility of griseofulvin relatives increased the fungicidal activity; and that apparently an optimum must exist among any group of such compounds representing a favorable balance between activity and penetrability.

With the introduction of the many new groups of organic compounds capable of being absorbed and translocated by plants with little or no phytotoxic effects it seems evident that an excellent set of reagents has been added to our stock of chemical translocation indicators. Used comparatively with other nontoxic compounds and normal plant constituents—that is, sugars—they constitute a set of invaluable tools for studying the uptake and distribution of substances by intact whole plants.

SECTION THREE

Mechanism of Solute Movement in the Phloem

chapter six

Structure and Function of Phloem

INTRODUCTION

Early work on translocation of assimilates in the phloem has been reviewed in Chapter 1. Long a controversial subject, the mechanics of this process is currently viewed as involving two possible physical processes: (1) diffusion accelerated in some way, or (2) mass or convectional flow. Because the phloem is a delicate tissue system, completely embedded in the plant body and surrounded by living cells whose life processes are ultimately related to their function, study of phloem function is difficult. Early works involving ringing, heat and cold treatment, gas treatments, use of dyes, and gross analyses of organs and tissues have provided a general picture of solute movement in the phloem but such methods cannot provide a final explanation of the mechanism because this is so easily disturbed. Probably the most valuable conclusion that can be drawn from these studies is that assimilates move in the phloem from source to sink and that rates are entirely beyond the possible range of simple diffusion.

The first breakthrough in this complex and difficult task came with the discovery that certain viruses, inoculated into the phloem by feeding insects, move along the same source-to-sink path as assimilates and that their movement could be controlled by the same procedures as have proved useful in manipulating food movement. Thus by ringing, shading, pruning, and controlled inoculation Bennett (1934, 1935, 1937) was able to show that the curly-top virus of beets was carried in the food stream, not along a virus gradient but along a food gradient. Esau (1938, 1941) by careful histological work demonstrated that the rapid movement of the virus takes place in the mature sieve tubes of the phloem. Subsequent work has proved that the rapid transport of many other viruses is confined to functioning sieve tubes. Thus the viruses prove to be excellent indicators of food movement in plants.

The second major advance came with the discovery that 2,4-D, a plant growth regulator, is absorbed by leaf cells, moved into the phloem, and translocated rapidly with foods. This uptake and distribution takes place in intact plants, and the presence of the tracer is manifested by tropic bending, malformation of leaves and roots, inhibition of growth, and, when large doses are used, death of the plant. All of these responses occur at a distance from the point of application and are taken as evidences of the movement of the tracer.

Current work with labeled tracers comes within the same category as the virus work in that these compounds are absorbed into the functioning phloem of intact plants, they very evidently follow the source-to-sink pattern of distribution, and they may be detected both by formative effects shown by the living plants and by autoradiography of freeze-dried plants.

Because it is impossible to extract the phloem and set it up as a demonstrable mechanism for controlled study, our only recourse is to collect as much circumstantial evidence for its mode of action as possible and try to fit the various observations together into a plausible scheme. There seems to be little hope of constructing a model that will prove beyond doubt the physical nature of the processes of assimilate transport.

This task of working at a distance, of fitting together many bits of circumstantial evidence, and of winnowing out the facts from various ill-founded ideas is a difficult one. Our experience indicates that more knowledge from many aspects is needed and that no bit of relevant evidence should be neglected. For this reason the subject will be taken up in parts, beginning with phloem structure, followed by the evidence from phloem exudation, and finally the current evidence from tracer studies.

PHLOEM STRUCTURE

The phloem tissue of most plants is composed of sieve elements, several kinds of parenchyma cells, fibers, and sclereids. In angiosperms companion cells accompany the sieve elements; in gymnosperms specialized parenchyma cells termed albuminous cells seem to be analogous to the companion cells. Albuminous cells and companion cells are obliterated together with accompanying sieve cells.

Sieve elements of the phloem are obviously the cells primarily involved in translocation. They are the cells most highly specialized; they are the cells from which phloem exudate comes; they are the cells that Schumacher demonstrated as transporting both carbohydrates and nitrogen (Schumacher, 1930).

The companion cells, commonly associated with the sieve tubes of angiosperms, have been described as retaining a nuclear influence over the sieve tubes after the latter have become enucleate (Esau, 1939). We know that the sieve tube and accompanying companion cell or cells arise from a common mother cell (Esau, 1939), that the companion cell retains its nucleus and dense cytoplasmic content throughout the functioning life of the sieve tube, and that the sieve tube and its companion cell or cells are obliterated together. Esau (1948) has found that the companion cells of grape have slime bodies similar to those found in the sieve tubes of this species.

Phloem parenchyma cells are often filled with starch and obviously function as storage cells. In leaves and stems of herbaceous plants they may contain chloroplasts. In leaves and green stems they may serve in the polar symplastic conduction of sugars to the sieve elements (Roeckl, 1949). In unpigmented phloem they undoubtedly play a role in symplastic movement of foods from sieve tubes to meristems or to storage cells. In the willow stems studied by Mittler (1957b) and Weatherley and his associates (1959) the phloem parenchyma cells undoubtedly supply the sugars and amino acids that maintain phloem movement in isolated stem segments.

Other than a possible function in strengthening, little can be said concerning phloem fibers. Fibers of flax and hemp, and many others of commercial importance, originate in the phloem. A wide array of sclereids also originates in the phloem, some coming directly from the cambium, others by late differentiation from phloem parenchyma.

Sieve-tube ontogeny

In primary phloem the young protophloem sieve tube becomes prominent by developing thick, darkly staining walls, and its contents usually acquire more than the usual amount of stain. In the secondary phloem, wall thickening and turgor expansion to a greater size than neighboring parenchyma cells characterize young sieve elements; often the thickened wall displays the shining nacre condition characteristic of developing sieve tubes of certain species.

The young sieve element is a nucleate cell of angular outline and active streaming protoplasm. Plastids are commonly present in the cytoplasm, and in many species slime bodies of various types may be found (Esau, 1953). In young sieve tubes an inner network of cytoplasmic strands may traverse the vacuole of the cell, and often the nucleus is suspended among these strands. Streaming is often observed in young sieve elements and it is most prominent in these strands. These young elements accumulate to a high degree vital dyes such as neutral red and they readily plasmolyze when treated with hypertonic solutions of sucrose, dextrose, or KNO_3. During ontogeny the sieve elements undergo rapid turgor expansion, crowding their neighbor parenchyma cells; they quickly enlarge to their mature size.

Throughout the intermediate stages of development the nucleus is present; slime bodies are present in the cytoplasm, often associated with the nucleus. In electron microscope views these are granular in structure and are bounded by a double membrane (Beer, 1959). Plastids present within the cytoplasm may accumulate starch that stains wine-red with iodine. Sieve cells of conifers may go through the winter in this intermediate stage of ontogeny, completing their maturation quickly with the increase in activity in the spring.

Having reached mature size, the sieve element undergoes a series of unique changes found in no other plant cells. These changes may go on very rapidly or more slowly; they may all go on at the same time or at different rates. When they are completed, the sieve element is an entirely different cell, and it is commonly assumed that it has reached its functional state. First in importance among these changes is the disintegration of the nucleus. This has been seen and described by many (Crafts, 1951) and it undoubtedly plays an important role in sieve-tube specialization.

Accompanying nuclear breakdown, the slime bodies disintegrate and disappear as discrete inclusions. It seems probable that much of the slimy, deep-staining material found in sieve tubes during intermediate stages of ontogeny and early stages of maturity results from this breakdown of nucleus and slime bodies. This material is termed slime and it is exuded through sieve plates and out of open sieve tubes onto the end of a stem when a transverse cut is made across a stem of cucurbit, grape, or a number of other species. The mature sieve tubes contain no mitochondria or endoplasmic reticulum (Beer, 1959). Spheroid bodies found in sieve cells of several species by Le Comte (1889), Crafts (1938), and Engard (1944) have been identified by Esau (1947) as nucleoli extruded during the breakdown of nuclei.

Plastids embedded in the cytoplasm of the young sieve tubes become much less firmly fixed and during sectioning may be displaced and migrate to the end of the cell with the slime.

Attending these cytologic changes in the sieve elements are cytoplasmic changes of equal magnitude. Streaming gradually slows down, becomes plastic or amoeboid, and finally stops. Neutral red does not accumulate but aniline blue will penetrate and stain callose on the sieve plates, even of plasmolyzed elements (Currier *et al.,* 1955). The cytoplasm becomes less fluid in consistency but remains highly sensitive to injury.

During this stage of maturation the sieve-tube cytoplasm may develop an avidity for dyes, which it later loses. However, because of this cytoplasm's great sensitivity to injury it is difficult to interpret its staining reactions; the high staining may be the result of disturbance. Meanwhile, during this stage, the endoplast or inner phase boundary (tonoplast) tends to disappear and in the functioning element the parietal layer of the cytoplasm can be seen only by special staining technic or by separation from the wall by plasmolysis, shrinking, or dehydration and staining (alcohol and IKI).

There has been a long controversy over the plasmolyzability of the mature sieve-tube element, some investigators (Huber, 1941; Crafts, 1939a, 1951) claiming that it could not be plasmolyzed; others (Curtis and Asai, 1939; Schumacher, 1939) claiming that it could. It remained for Currier, Esau, and Cheadle (1955) to resolve the controversy. They proved that, by using proper technics including constant contact with sucrose solution, mature sieve tubes of some 22 species could be plasmolyzed and that some could be carried through 5 to 7 cycles of plasmolysis and deplasmolysis. *Vitis* proved to be the best material for these studies, and they plasmolyzed sieve tubes of this species in both dormant and active condition. In addition to plasmolysis, Currier, Esau, and Cheadle observed a movement of particles within the sieve-tube lumina that they termed "surge." This they attributed to rapid displacement of the sieve-tube sap brought about by changing turgor. They consider this to be evidence for mass flow in the sieve tubes and they discuss the permeability relations of the sieve-tube cytoplasm, particularly that of the sieve plate.

Swanson (1946) described the reactions of plant tissues to sprays containing 0.1 percent 2,4-D and stated that sieve tubes were not responsive whereas parenchyma of the endodermis, phloem, cambium, and rays were active in cell proliferation; this is further evidence for their specialization.

During the functioning period in the life of the sieve element the protoplasmic connections between the adjoining elements, across both side and end walls, are highly developed and prominent if properly stained. Although they are known to be composed of cytoplasm (Hepton *et al.,* 1955), their frequency and development suggests specialization for the function of assimilate distribution.

During the maturation stages, callose cylinders develop around these connections, and as the sieve tubes age these enlarge and elongate, finally merging to form the definitive callose. The protoplasmic connections that traverse the sieve plates are compressed, becoming smaller in diameter and stretched in length. Finally, at obliteration of the sieve element the callose may be dissolved away and the empty sieve-tube lumen filled with air.

The effective functioning life of the sieve cell varies within wide limits. The narrow protophloem element in the root or shoot tip or in young leaves may function for only a few days. Metaphloem elements function for longer periods, of weeks or months. Secondary elements, differentiated from cambium, function for the greater part of a growing season; in some species—notably grape (Esau, 1948a), *Tilia,* and *Liriodendron*—they may function a second year (Esau, 1953). With obliteration of the sieve elements, the phloem parenchyma cells continue to function in storage, often becoming enlarged and filled with ergastic substances. Other changes involve formation of sclereids and fibers, specialization of crystal- and tannin-bearing cells, intrusion or intensified development of laticiferous systems, and the common formation of successive cork cambium layers.

The sieve-tube protoplast

With the plasmolyzability of the mature sieve element firmly established, the search for the mechanism of phloem transport necessarily turns to the specialized nature of the sieve-element protoplast. The loss of the endoplast seems well established; the boundary between the mesoplasm and the vacuole is very indefinite; and the ectoplast must remain functional and partake of the nature of a semipermeable membrane. Rouschal (1941) concluded that the side-wall cytoplasmic layer must remain semipermeable but that the sieve area is highly permeable. To prove this he experimented with changing turgor conditions of sectioned *Aesculus* phloem and found displacement of starch grains comparable with the surge mentioned by Currier, Esau, and Cheadle (1955). These experiments are reminiscent of an observation of Crafts (1938, p. 795). By cutting away a tangential slice from the stem of an intact squash plant, thus laying bare the phloem, one may observe, by reflected light, the coagulation of the sieve-tube sap in the tubes. This occurs most rapidly in elements injured by cutting but slowly extends inward. If uncut sieve-tube elements are quickly flattened with a round instrument, the sieve plates are deformed, the cupped shape being reversed if the pressure is increased on the convex side. This response indicates resistance to very rapid flow. The sieve plates of successive elements at increasing distance from the point of deformation show successively less disturbance, however, indicating an elasticity and flexibility of the elements and the capacity for rapid adjustment of turgor changes by mass flow of sap.

If during maturation the endoplasts of the sieve-tube elements break down but the outer plasma membrane retains its semipermeability, rapid longitudinal flow of sap must take place across sieve plates via the protoplasmic connections. This requires that these connections become highly permeable in order to accommodate the rates of flow that have been observed. On the other hand, it would reconcile the existence of air-filled intercellular spaces that have been reported by Münch (1930, p. 55) and Martens and

Pigneur (1947) to occur in the phloem, and the possible occurrence of mature sieve elements directly adjacent to xylem elements found in certain monocot leaves by Esau (1953, p. 428).

The possibility that longitudinal transport of the assimilate stream is limited to the protoplasmic connections of the sieve plate or sieve area brings into bold relief another concept concerning phloem structure—namely, the phylogeny of the sieve tubes. Huber (1939) suggests that the phylogenetic development of the phloem has progressed from long-membered sieve tubes ($>550\mu$) with strongly inclined, scalariform pitted fine-porous plates to short-membered tubes (Robinia 135μ) with transverse wide-meshed plates.

In some survey work done several years ago the length of sieve elements in a number of woody gymnosperms and angiosperms was measured. Table 6-1 presents the results and serves to emphasize this relation. Of 58 gymnosperm species the elements averaged 1.40 mm in length; of 15 angiosperms the average was 0.450 mm with a range in the latter from 0.959 to 0.142.

This progress from long narrow elements with sloping walls to short broad ones with transverse walls would seem to be in the direction of greater efficiency, because as the sieve-plate strands increase in diameter they increase exponentially in area. If the cross-sectional area of each strand is made up of an outer lining of semipermeable membrane enclosing a more permeable core, and if the thickness of the membrane is constant, then the area of the core decreases very rapidly as the diameter of the strand approaches a value of two times the membrane thickness. In pine the strands of the sieve areas are around 0.1μ in diameter, in squash around 5μ. If we assume a common membrane thickness of 200 Å and calculate the proportion of the strand occupied by membrane versus core, the figures turn out to be 64 percent membrane and 36 percent core for white pine; 1.5 percent membrane and 98.5 percent core for squash.

Cheadle and Whitford (1941), in an exhaustive study of metaphloem sieve tubes of 126 species of 99 genera in 22 families of monocots, came to the conclusion that the phylogenetic specialization of structure in sieve tubes of the metaphloem involves (1) the progressive localization of highly specialized sieve areas on the end walls, (2) a gradual change from the very oblique to the transversely placed end walls, (3) a gradual change from compound to simple sieve plates, and (4) a progressive change in the sieve areas on the

Table 6-1

Lengths of Sieve Elements of the Secondary Phloem of Some Woody Plants

Gymnosperms			Angiosperms	
Genus	Species No.	Length average of 10 elements per species	Genus	Length average of 100 elements per species
		mm		mm
Abieteae			*Cercydiphylum*	.959
Pseudotsuga	2	1.80	*Liriodendron*	.861
Pinus	14	1.58	*Juglans*	.746
Abies	10	1.30	*Gryselinia*	.547
Cedrus	2	1.27	*Arbutus*	.401
Picea	6	1.25	*Eucalyptus*	.390
Taxodieae			*Casuarina*	.383
Cunninghamia	1	1.74	*Gordonia*	.376
Sequoia	2	1.34	*Aesculus*	.364
Cryptomeria	3	1.14	*Drimys*	.353
Taxodium	2	2.22	*Fraxinus*	.351
Cupresseae			*Ailanthus*	.331
Libocedrus	1	1.32	*Catalpa*	.308
Thuja	2	1.03	*Hedycarya*	.240
Cupressus	7	1.13	*Gossypium*	.142
Chamaecyparis	2	1.44	Average	.450
Juniperus	4	1.07		
Total	58	Average 1.40		

side walls of adjacent sieve-tube members in which the areas become less and less conspicuous. They consider that the distribution of the various types of sieve tubes in the different parts of the plant has phylogenetic significance and taken with the trend noted in (1) to (4) above "indicates that the position of the end wall is probably a factor in the efficiency of food conduction in the phloem of the Monocotyledoneae." Esau discusses the relation of the shape of sieve tubes to function (Esau, 1950, pp. 90–91) but comes to no definite conclusion. In a recent paper Esau, Cheadle, and Gifford (1953) state "There is some indication that the dicotyledonous sieve-tube elements show trends of specialization similar to those of the monocotyledons."

The crux of this problem seems to lie in the physical nature of the cytoplasm of the protoplasmic connections of the sieve plate. By electron microscopy Hepton *et al.* (1955) have shown that these connections are composed of solid cytoplasm and they conclude that the pores in the walls are completely plugged. The size of any presumptive micropores within the strands, they say, is an open question. In their electron micrographs the strands have obviously shrunk to approximately half their original diameter; hence they appear very dense. When we consider that phloem exudation takes place by mass movement of a solution through these strands we must face the fact that they are sufficiently permeable to allow a flow of solution at a linear velocity of 200 to 500 cm per hour. This would appear to indicate that they do contain micropores.

Table 6-2

Percent of Transverse Sieve-element Area Occupied by Pores and Strands

Sieve-plate group	Mean areas per sieve plate, μ^2		Percent of transverse cell area occupied by	
	pores	strands	pores	strands
Simple	793.1	469.6	83.2	49.3
Simple and scalariform	821.9	364.7	104.8	46.5
Scalariform	1111.0	315.1	112.9	32.0

With the light of inquiry now thrown on the strands of the sieve plate, work by Esau and Cheadle (1959) on the size and numbers of these assumes great significance. Earlier calculations indicated that the strands in the sieve plate of squash occupy about 8 percent of the sieve-plate area (Crafts, 1931), of potato 2.3 percent (Crafts, 1933). Esau and Cheadle measured areas of sieve plates, callose cylinders, and connecting strands in 160 species of dicots from 129 genera and 60 families. They grouped the plants into three groups: (a) those having 90 percent or more simple sieve plates, (b) simple and scalariform sieve plates with 11 to 89 percent simple, and (c) scalariform, 90 percent of the latter.

Table 6-2 reports their results on percent of transverse cell area occupied by pores and strands of sieve plates in 10 species in each of the three groups.

Since the transverse area was measured horizontally whereas the scalariform ends were sloping, it was possible for the pores to occupy more than 100 percent of the transverse area, which they did in groups (b) and (c).

Of particular interest, however, is the fact that the strands occupied the greatest proportionate area—49.3 percent in the case of the simple plates, 46.5 percent for the mixed group, and only 32 percent in the sloping scalariform plates. These values contrast with much smaller ones reported by Crafts (1931, 1933) for squash and potato; a variation that pinpoints the problem of measuring protoplasmic connections in their natural state. Phloem cell walls are highly hydrated (Crafts, 1931) and the protoplasm consists principally of water. Furthermore, within the intact plant the sieve-tube contents inside the ectoplasm are inflated by turgor pressure. It seems probable that the above differences may be due partly at least to differences in methods in preparation. Whatever the reason, the large ratio of strand area to sieve-tube transverse area is very encouraging, for it indicates a much lower velocity of flow through these strands than was used in previous calculations.

Some drawings from some slides of *Cucurbita* may further elucidate the nature of sieve-tube cytoplasm, slime bodies, slime, sieve-tube sap and its coagulation, and slime sacs—structures long known but little understood by plant physiologists.

Fig. 6-1a shows a young sieve tube in the slime-drop stage; the slime drops are beginning to enlarge and merge. Fig. 6-1b shows a similar cell at a little later stage; Fig. 6-1c, still later. In Fig. 6-1c the nucleus in the element above the sieve plate is expanding; the slime drops have merged into large masses.

Fig. 6-1d shows a sieve tube in which the slime drops have almost completely disintegrated; in the upper portion the enlarged nucleus is about to lose its boundary membrane; on the upper right is a sieve plate with amassed coagulated slime. Fig. 6-1e shows an element with slime on the upper and lower sides of the sieve plate. The slime is completely amorphous but not densely coagulated. The cell contents have shrunk from dehydration.

Fig. 6-2a shows a sieve tube entering the permeable phase. The cut end of the section is at the bottom and slime has accumulated on the distal side of the plate. Coagulation has occurred in three connections that are permeated by slime. Fig. 6-2b shows a sieve plate near the cut end of the section. Coagulated slime is amassed

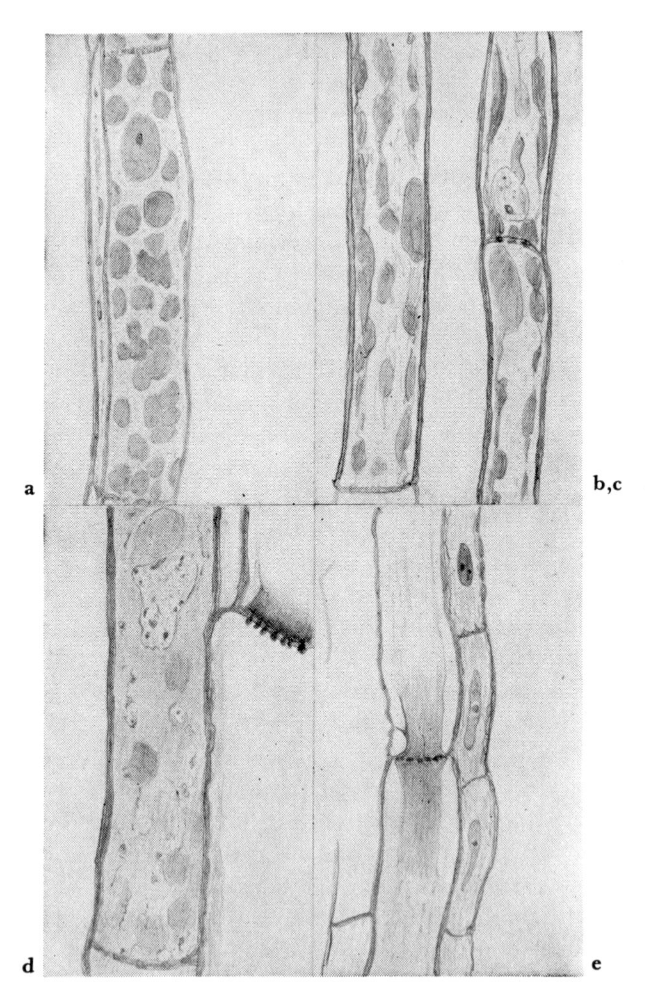

Fig. 6-1. Ontogeny of the cucurbit sieve tube. a, young sieve tube in the slime drop stage; nucleus with nucleolus near the top. b and c, successively later stages. The nucleus in c is expanding and the slime drops are enlarged and disintegrating. d, the nucleus is greatly expanded, many slime drops have disintegrated, and the sieve plate at the upper right is layered on the distal side with slime. e, mature elements with contents somewhat shrunken by dehydration. The slime is now amorphous and it tends to accumulate at the sieve plate; companion cells on the right of the sieve tube, phloem parenchyma on the left.

on the plate; slime permeates the connections and may be seen streaming to the cut end where it adheres to the cut cell walls. Fig. 6-3 shows slime accumulated above two sieve plates and streams running from the upper plate to the lower one.

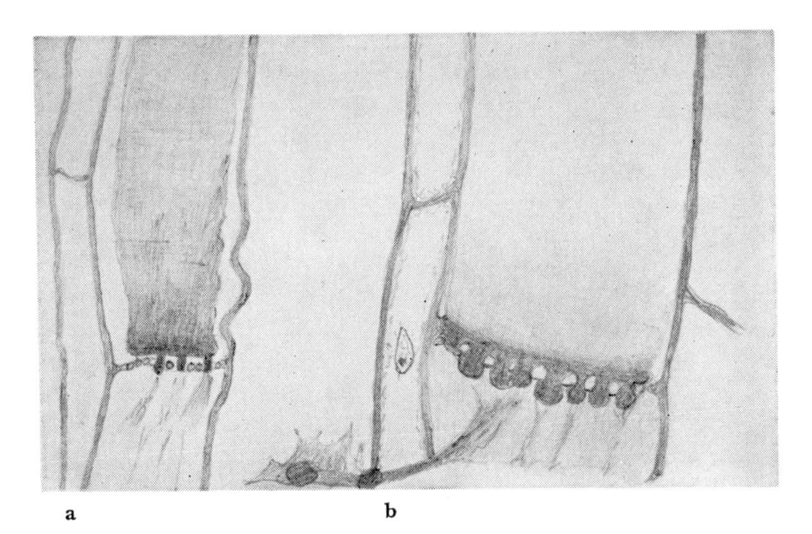

Fig. 6-2. Cucurbit sieve tubes entering the permeable phase. a, slime accumulated on the distal side of a sieve plate, the result of cutting the stem and subsequent rapid flow toward the cut end. The sieve plate acts as a filter to hold back the larger molecules of slime. b, sieve plate with coagulated slime, slime permeating the sieve strands, and coagulated slime on the cut end of the section (lower end).

Fig. 6-4 shows four views of slime sacs formed on the proximal sides of sieve plates that are near the cut ends of sections. Fig. 6-4a shows a sac filled with coagulated slime; Fig. 6-4b, a sac partially filled with slime; Fig. 6-4c and d, sacs filled with sieve-tube sap—6-4c being a double sac and 6-4d a single highly inflated sac.

The sacs shown here are interpreted as indicating that the protoplasmic connections of the sieve plate are solid and consist at a certain stage of a fluid, viscous, elastic cytoplasm. When the highly turgid system is cut across, the tremendous steepening of the pressure gradient at the cut surface causes a very rapid exudation. The sacs shown in Fig. 6-4 are localized almost entirely on the sieve plates exposed by the cut and they are always on the proximal side of the exposed plate. They apparently result from

Fig. 6-3. A sieve element with streams of slime running from the upper to the lower sieve plate; cut end of section at the bottom.

the pushing through of the fluid cytoplasm of the sieve-plate strand and inflation with sieve-tube sap containing varying amounts of slime. Note that all plates do not have these sacs.

Fig. 6-5 shows three sieve plates. Fig. 6-5a is a plate with its connections variously impregnated with coagulated slime. Several connections near the top of the group show as gray areas with black centers. These are interpreted as cytoplasmic strands with strands of coagulated slime permeating their center regions. The larger black regions are strands completely impregnated with coagulated slime. Those with the white centers have rings of coagulated slime surrounding cores of cytoplasm or possibly pores resulting from the forcing through of sieve-tube sap. Fig. 6-5b is a view of sieve plates with and without slime accumulations, below a plate cleared of slime in the cutting process. The light areas represent the total space occupied by connections with their callose cylinders (pores).

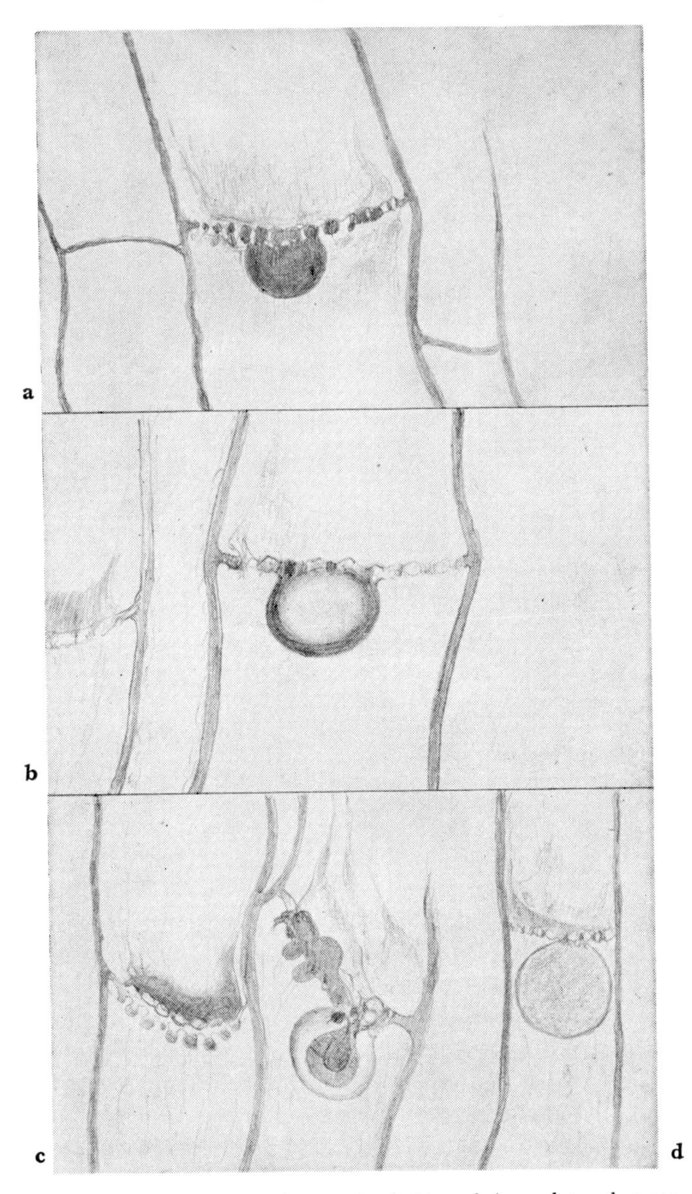

Fig. 6-4. Slime sacs on the proximal sides of sieve plates that are near the cut ends of sections. Rapid phloem exudation has taken place through these sieve plates and certain sieve-plate strands have been pushed through and inflated with sieve-tube sap containing slime. a, sac completely filled with slime; b, sac partially filled with slime; c, compound sac with coagulated slime inside the cytoplasmic sheath; d, a single highly inflated sac.

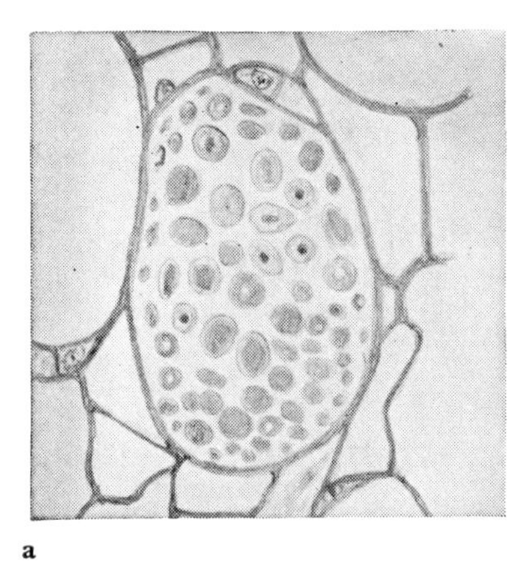

a

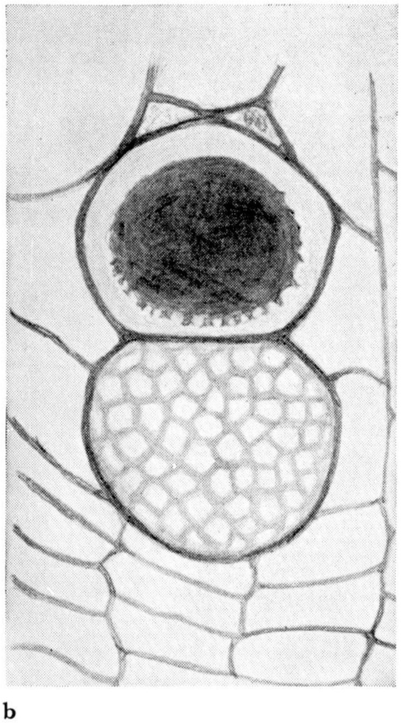

b

Fig. 6-5. Sieve plates showing strands, callose cylinders, and the cellulose mesh. a, sieve plate in a transverse section with its strands variously impregnated with slime. The dark centers represent impregnation by slime; the light centers are probably caused by a cut across the plate and removal of the inflated portions of plates as shown in Fig. 6-2. Such strands are probably tubular but they represent artifacts resulting from rapid phloem exudation caused by cutting. b (above), slime accumulation; (below), cellulose mesh of a sieve plate cleared of slime and cytoplasm.

It is proposed here that this phenomenon of impregnation of sieve-tube connections by slime and its coagulation in the killing and fixing process is the one termed "pushing through" by Hill and "Durchbrechung" by Rouschal.

Fig. 6-6 is a comparison of sieve areas on squash and white pine; Fig. 6-6a shows a sieve plate with its protoplasmic connections impregnated with coagulated slime. The connections are surrounded by callose cylinders suspended in a cellulose matrix. This view and those presented in Figs. 6-2 and 6-3 seem to indicate rather definitely that the sieve-plate connections are permeable to slime at this stage of maturity. Fig. 6-6b shows sieve areas of white pine at the same magnification as 6-6a. Fig. 6-7a and b pictures sieve areas of white pine; Fig. 6-7c and d, redwood on edge to show the extremely tenuous nature of the protoplasmic connections.

From this brief review of phloem structure it is evident that

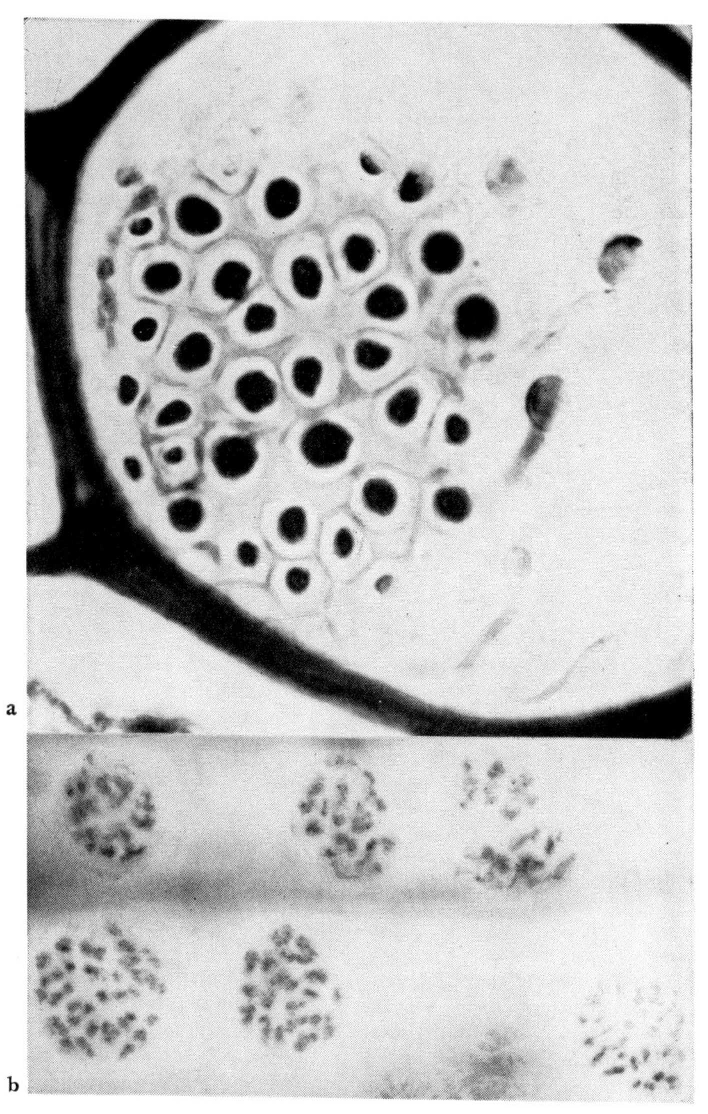

Fig. 6-6. Sieve plates of squash (a) and white pine (b) in surface view (× 2000). The sieve strands of squash are impregnated with slime, which makes them stain densely. Each protoplasmic strand is surrounded by a callose cylinder. The sieve strands of white pine are very fine and each group is embedded in a callose cylinder. The gray spots in each sieve area are the callose cylinders; the small dark spots are the protoplasmic strands.

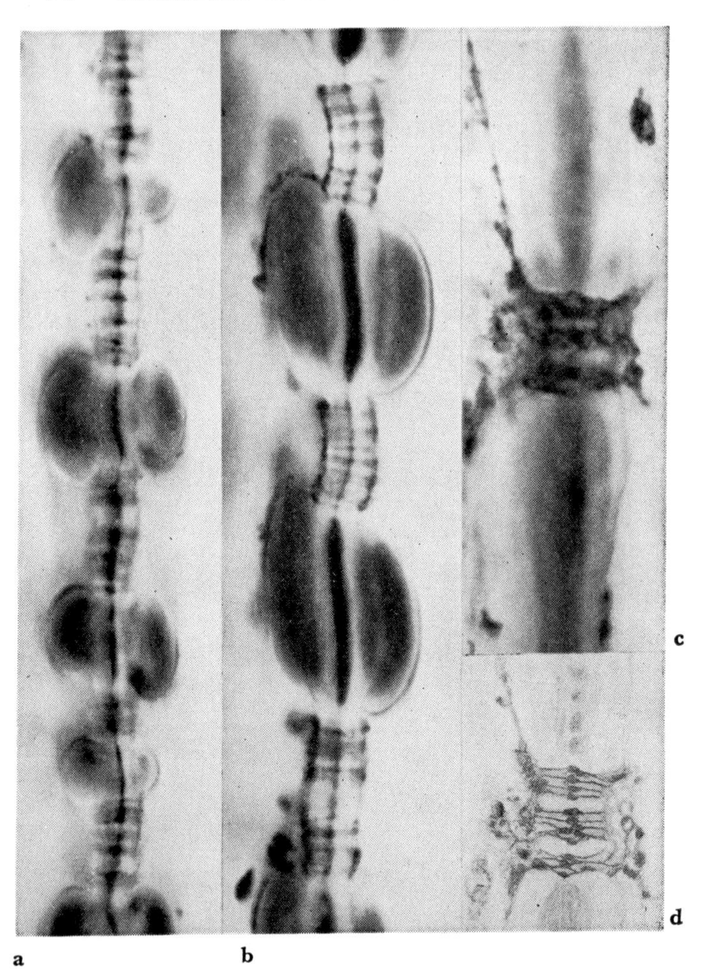

Fig. 6-7. Sieve areas of white pine and redwood on edge to show the very tenuous protoplasmic strands (× 2000). a and b, white pine, *Pinus strobus*. c and d, redwood, *Sequoia sempervirens*. d, a drawing to show the nature of the complex sieve strands of redwood as seen under the microscope. The sections shown have been swollen with sulfuric acid, stained with iodine and water soluble aniline blue, and mounted in glycerine.

the rapid flow of solution through the sieve-tube system presents some difficult problems. In this connection two well-substantiated facts stand out: (1) the profound change that takes place in the sieve-tube protoplast with the loss of nucleus and other changes attending maturation, and (2) the rapid flow of sap from cut phloem. This latter phenomenon will now be examined.

PHLOEM EXUDATION

Manifestations of phloem exudation have been known since ancient times. Keller (1956) explains that the manna of the scriptures is the dry honeydew produced by a shell-backed plant louse that grows on the tamarisk, a leguminous shrub indigenous to the region of Mount Sinai. Manna can be found on the list of exports from the Sinai peninsula and is commonly collected by monks and Arabs and sold to pilgrims. It is sweet like honey, is attractive to ants, and sticks to the teeth. It has a crystalline consistency.

Huber (1953) tells of a small industry in southern Italy that derives income from manna made from sieve-tube exudate of *Fraxinus ornus* and *F. excelsior*. The trees are tapped by making sloping cuts across the bark. The exudate dries in the arid climate and the sugar is collected and sold. Collections are made throughout the summer and early autumn. The tapping areas are rotated around the stems so that the trees may be used for years.

Honeydew is known to all people familiar with aphids, mealy bugs, and similar insects that feed from the phloem of plants. Leonhardt (1940), using a single insect, counted the number of droplets produced per hour through a 24-hour period. There proved to be a diurnal fluctuation in honeydew production, coinciding with assimilation values found by Huber, Schmidt, and Jahnel (1937).

Kennedy and Mittler (1953) reported that the mouth parts of the lachnid *Tuberolachnus salignum* that feeds on willow could be severed and the resulting exudate collected at a rate of about one cubic mm per hour for periods up to four days. Mittler (1953) reported that the amino acid content of phloem sap is higher than that of honeydew, indicating that these acids are extracted from the sap as it passes through the insect. The following amino acids and amides could be demonstrated by chromatography in both phloem sap and honeydew: aspartic acid, glutamic acid, serine, threonine, alanine, valine, leucine and/or isoleucine, phenylalanine, asparagine, glutamine, and possibly γ-amino butyric acid. These could be found during initial growth and during senescence when proteins are known to be hydrolyzed and moved out of leaves.

During the intervening period all that could be found were small amounts of aspartic and glutamic acids and their amides. The periods of initial growth and of senescence are preferred by certain leaf-feeding aphids, presumably because leaves at these times afford the insects nitrogen-rich phloem sap.

Mittler (1957a) found that *Tuberolachnus salignus* feeds on the newly differentiated sieve tubes of the phloem of willow. From tests on phloem exudation through cut stylets he concluded that the insect does not suck but relies upon the pressure in the sieve tubes to force the sap through its stylets. It must swallow actively in order to ingest the sap. Table 6-3 (Mittler 1957b) presents data on stylet-sap exudation from willow.

Table 6-3

Stylet-sap Exudation from the Severed Stylet Bundle of a Second and Third Instar Nymph

Instar	Period of exudation hours	Total volume exuded mm^3	Average rate of exudation mm^3 1 hr	Total sugar concentration percent w per v
Second	0–25	18.14	0.73	8.60
	25–41	28.89	0.67	
	41–72	49.34	0.66	8.50
Third	0–18	21.75	1.21	8.51
	18–35	19.35	1.14	8.43
	35–56	18.95	0.91	8.31
	56–76	17.80	0.89	8.38
	76–100	21.10	0.88	8.18

During bud swelling the total nitrogen concentration of the exudate was 0.2 percent w per v; during bud burst and start of leaf growth it was 0.12 percent; during the period of maturity it dropped to below 0.03 percent; and during senescence it rose again to 0.13 percent. These concentrations seem well correlated with the known organic nitrogen nutrition of the tree as provided by phloem transport. As mentioned, a part of this nitrogen is extracted by the insects; the sugar concentration of the honeydew did not differ from that of stylet sap by more than 5 percent.

From a careful analysis of the literature and from his own investigations Mittler concludes that water, amino acids, amides, and sucrose pass en masse through the sieve tubes of a willow stem toward the sieve tube tapped by the stylets. It seems reasonable to conclude that these same compounds make up the stylet sap and hence the food source of the insect. From 1 to 4 mg of sucrose per day are used by a single insect, an amount equivalent to the photosynthetic product of 5 to 20 cm^2 of leaf surface during 10 hours.

Fig. 6-8. A branch of the carob tree (*Ceratonia siliqua*) showing work of the red-breasted sap-sucker (*Sphyrapicus varius*). The bird perforates the bark down to the active phloem and phloem exudation takes place from the perforations.

Aphids are not the only insects that feed on phloem exudate; leaf hoppers, mealy bugs, coccids, and others make use of this rich source of organic foods. Fig. 6-8 shows a portion of a branch of *Ceratonia siliqua,* the carob tree, that has been perforated down to the active phloem by the red-breasted sap-sucker, *Sphyrapicus varius.* Exudation from this punctured bark was observed for over three weeks during March of 1959 at Davis, California. The bird was seen to be working on several occasions, and more holes were made from day to day. Fig. 6-9 shows the large area on the sidewalk beneath the branch, wet by the sugary exudate. During wet weather the exudate was a thin, sweet liquid; during dry weather it dried on leaves and on the sidewalk below. Exudation was most rapid during bright, warm days. *Ceratonia siliqua* is an evergreen tree and was in full foliage in March.

Hartig reported on the exudation of sap from cut stems of cucurbits over 100 years ago; these studies have been continued by Zacharias (1884), Kraus (1885), Fisher (1883, 1884), Le Comte (1889),

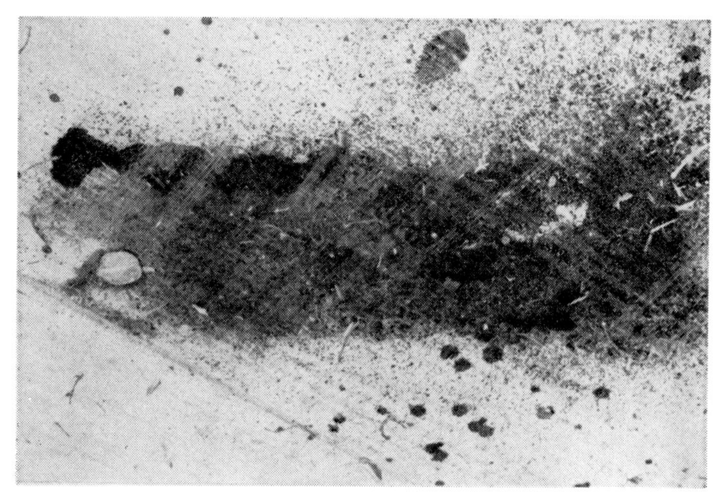

Fig. 6-9. Area of sidewalk beneath the branch shown in Fig. 6-8. During dry weather the sugary sap dries to a sticky coating. Note the imprints of bicycle wheels that have passed over the area. Dimensions of the area are approximately 1 by 3 ft.

Haberlandt (1914), Münch (1930), Crafts (1931, 1932, 1936, 1939a), Huber, Schmidt, and Jahnel (1937), Moose (1938), Tingley (1944), and others.

Crafts and Lorenz (1944a, b) proved that phloem exudate from cucurbits is not a true sample of the assimilate stream, for it contains an excess of nitrogenous material. The carbon-nitrogen ratios of exudate from stem tips and from peduncles of fruits of widely varying sizes were remarkably constant and always one-third to one-fifth that of fruits. The differences lay in the high nitrogen of the exudate. Crafts (1948) attempted to explain this content on the assumption that the high velocity of the sap stream immediately following cutting (up to 11 times normal flow rates, Crafts, 1933) frees nitrogen residues from the altered cytoplasm of the mature sieve tubes and sweeps them out in the exudate. Crafts (1954) reported that the nitrogenous substances of cucurbit phloem exudate consist of complex compounds unidentifiable by ninhydrin; hydrolyzed exudate contained proline, leucine, isoleucine, norleucine, phenylalanine, valine, tyrosine, alanine, glutamic acid, aspartic

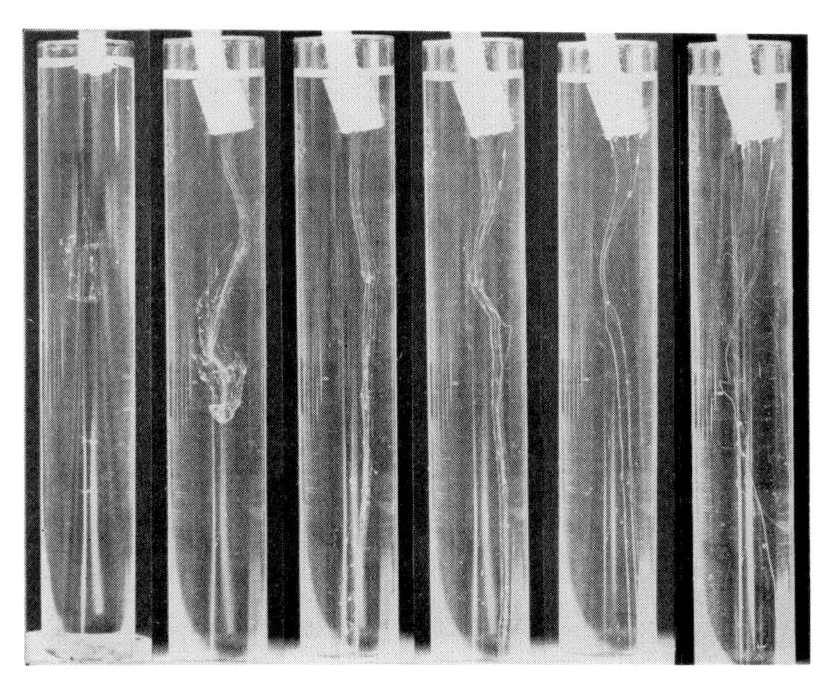

Fig. 6-10. Flow of phloem exudate from the cut end of a squash stem into 50 percent alcohol. The exudate coagulates in the alcohol and appears as a series of white threads proceeding from the phloem groups of the bicollateral bundles of the stem. Time series (left to right) 10 sec, 18 sec, 30 sec, 60 sec, 90 sec, 120 sec.

acid, cystine or cysteine, serine, threonine, and possibly arginine and glycine. Fig. 6-10 shows phloem exudate flowing from the cut stem of squash into 50 percent alcohol.

Analyses by Moose (1938) and Huber, Schmidt, and Jahnel (1937) indicate that the phloem exudates from trees more closely resemble the normal composition of assimilates carried in the phloem. The data of Mittler (Table 6-3), Wanner (1953a), Ziegler (1956), and Zimmermann (1958) support the same view.

Wanner and Ziegler report sucrose as the only sugar found

chromatographically in the phloem exudate of 12 species of trees. Zimmermann found raffinose and stachyose in addition to sucrose in phloem exudate of *Liriodendron* and white ash. Sucrose predominated in the exudate of 14 tree species.

The sugar palm is another source of phloem exudate (Tammes, 1957). Bose (1923) reports that the palm *Arenga saccharifera* may exude as much as 4 liters per day from an incision; *Phoenix dactylifera,* 10 liters. Sap is drawn by tapping the upper end of the trunk, the lower leaves having been removed. The side of the tree facing the sun is wounded and a V-groove is made spiraling around the trunk; a small drain is inserted and an earthen pot hung beneath. The trees are evergreen and tapping is done from November to February in India; during the hotter season exudation is reduced and there is more difficulty with fermentation. The palmyra palm (*Borassus flabellifer*) is tapped by wounding the spadices and then cutting off the tip of each. Bose reports collecting 2100 ml per day from one spadix and 11 liters from all spadices on a single tree. The sap may contain 0.25 percent mineral solids and 10 percent sugar. Exudation is most rapid from midnight till dawn and slowest after noon, indicating that it arises as a result of osmosis and its volume is correlated inversely with water stress. The tree shows no root pressure at the time. Tammes gives the following composition for sieve-tube sap of *Arenga saccharifera:*

Sucrose: About 15 percent
Other sugars: None
Nitrogen: Total 410 mg per liter. Amino acids-glutamic acid, alanine, serine, arginine, methionine, and threonine. Total ± 40 mg per liter. Remainder unknown.
Potash: 1200 mg per liter of K^+
Phosphate: 98 mg per liter PO_4^{3-}
Magnesium: 96 mg per liter of Mg^{2+}
Calcium: 10 mg per liter of Ca^{2+}

From these various lines of endeavor it seems that phloem exudation may be taken as direct evidence for the longitudinal permeability of the sieve-tube system, and its composition as an indication of the composition of the assimilate stream. Obviously, when an inflated, elastic system of this sort is cut and exposed to pressure of only one atmosphere, the outflow will be greatly accelerated and its direction from one of the ends completely reversed.

Obvious also is the fact that resistance to flow from the elements near the cut end is much less than resistance from a greater distance; osmotic adjustment in the form of entry of water from surrounding cells is also rapid.

All of these phenomena account for the rapidity of initial exudation that may take place at a rate as high as 11 times the rate of flow of the assimilate stream (Crafts, 1931). They also account for the dilution of the sap noted in the collections of Crafts (1936), Cooil (1941), Tingley (1944), and Zimmermann (1958). The demonstration by Colwell (1942b) of radioactivity in phloem exudate of squash, the leaf of which had been treated critically with $P^{32}O_4$, indicates that this nutrient may be absorbed through the leaf and transported in the assimilate stream. This is the forerunner of a great amount of valuable work with the labeled tracers in translocation research.

SECTION FOUR

Movement of Assimilates and Indicators

chapter seven

Movement of Assimilates

Studies on assimilate movement in plants have attacked the problem from many angles. Hull (1952) studied the absorption and translocation of applied glucose and sucrose in tomato and sugar beet plants. He found glucose to be the more rapidly absorbed of the two sugars and translocation of both sugars to be rapid, a result that is supported by experiments of Vernon and Aronoff (1952). Hull found that local chilling of the stem of tomato, and chilling of whole beet seedlings brought about an equal or greater translocation than that in control plants at normal temperature. Böhning *et al.* (1953), on the other hand, found, in local temperature control experiments, that translocation increased in a linear fashion through the series 12°, 18°, and 24° C. A 30° C temperature treatment reduced translocation somewhat over the 24° C treatment.

Gauch and Duggar (1953), in studying the role of boron in the translocation of sucrose, show that small concentrations of boron greatly facilitate the absorption and transport of applied sucrose. They propose that the boron reacts with the sugar to form a sugar-borate complex that is ionizable. This complex apparently moves through cellular membranes more readily than nonborated sucrose. Inside the plant the ionized sugar complex seems to move readily to regions where assimilates are being rapidly used in respiration and growth.

Mitchell, Dugger, and Gauch (1953) have shown that applied boron greatly enhances translocation of 2,4-D, 3-indole acetic acid, 2,4,5-trichlorophenoxyacetic acid, and α-naphthalene acetic acid when the latter are applied with sucrose to the leaves of bean plants. In three preliminary tests on plants in the dark, translocation of 2,4-D was increased by approximately 43, 47, and 50 percent by boron in the applied sugar solution as compared with sugar solution alone. In later experiments in the light, boron, 2,4-D, and sugar were used separately and in all possible combinations on greenhouse-grown plants. Results were, in degrees of stem curvature, 13.2 for 2,4-D (0.9 gamma, NH_4 salt) alone; 3.3 for 2,4-D plus sucrose; 44.7 for 2,4-D plus sucrose plus boron; and 28.2 for 2,4-D plus boron. The last figure indicates the effect of applied boron on movement of naturally occurring sugar and hence on 2,4-D movement. Boron application increased curvature from indole acetic acid treatment by 1120 percent; from 2,4,5-T treatment 356 percent; and from α-naphthalene acetic acid treatment by 115 percent. Comparing sugars, they found increases of 235, 427, and 1520 percent in stem curvatures from applications with boron and 2,4-D of sucrose, fructose, and glucose, respectively.

Sisler, Duggar, and Gauch (1956) continued the studies on the role of boron in the translocation of sugars. Using tomato plants grown in culture solutions, they studied the movement of applied sugars in boron-sufficient and boron-deficient plants. Applying sugar solutions and sugar plus boron solutions through cut petioles of the two groups, they found that plants grown in the absence of boron, but not yet showing boron-deficiency symptoms, translocated more sucrose when 50 ppm of boron were added than when sucrose alone was applied. Normal plants grown with 0.5 ppm boron in the culture solution did not show a consistent increase when boron was included in the treatment solution. Plants showing boron-deficiency symptoms took up less sucrose. The addition of boron did not facilitate transport of sugar. Boron appeared to have its effect in facilitating sugar transport only before morphological symptoms became evident.

After 4 hours of exposure to $C^{14}O_2$, boron-sufficient plants translocated a greater percentage of the radioactive photosynthate produced than did boron-deficient plants. After 20 minutes exposure, the same relation held for plants growing on boron-sufficient and boron-deficient cultures for varying periods up to 14 days. Differences in all these cases were rather small but their consistency seemed to indicate significance.

Duggar *et al.* (1957) from studies on the influence of boron on starch phosphorylase proposed that one of the ways in which boron may bring about an increase in translocation of sugars in plants is by decreasing the enzymatic conversion of glucose-1-phosphate to starch. With an increase in the steady state concentration of glucose-1-phosphate, the amount available for other reactions, such as the synthesis of sucrose, may increase. Any increase in these soluble carbohydrates *in situ* may increase translocation from source to sink.

From the review of literature it is evident that more and more exact methods of analysis are coming into use in translocation research. Isotopic and chromatographic technics have provided impetus for new studies on translocation. Swanson (1957) and Swanson and El-Shishing (1958), using $C^{14}O_2$ in tracer studies, have shown that transport of sugars in grape canes from the youngest fully expanded leaf toward the shoot tip took place at a rate of 60 cm per hour and was in the phloem. Although sucrose, glucose, and fructose were present in the stem samples analyzed, Swanson concluded that sucrose was the sugar that moved, the hexoses resulting from conversion. The same sugars were present in lesser quantities in the xylem, and Swanson states that these were transferred laterally from the phloem.

Swanson reviews current literature with reference to his conclusion that sucrose is the only sugar transported in the phloem. He cites the work of Wanner and Mittler, already reported, in support of his conclusion and contrasts it with the interpretation of Vernon and Aronoff (1952) that sucrose, glucose, and fructose were all moved in soybean. He stresses the importance of the source-sink relationship of phloem transport.

Zimmermann (1957a) has made valuable contributions to our knowledge of phloem function. Analyzing phloem exudate from 16 tree species of 11 families, he has found not only sucrose, but raffinose, stachyose, and verbascose. Table 7-1 presents some of his results.

In a second paper Zimmermann (1957b) sets up three basic requirements for the mass-flow mechanism: (1) the cytoplasm lining the longitudinal walls of the sieve tubes must be semipermeable; (2) the sieve plates, however, must be permeable to the translocated

Table 7-1

Sugars in Sieve-tube Exudate of Some American Trees

Family	Name of tree	Sucrose	Raffinose	Stachyose	Verbascose
Salicaceae	Aspen (*Populus tremuloides*)	xxx	tr	tr	–
Fagaceae	Beech (*Fagus grandifolia*)	xxx	tr	–	–
	Chestnut (*Castanea dentata*)	xxx	tr	–	–
	White oak (*Quercus alba*)	xxx	–	–	–
	Chestnut oak (*Quercus prinus*)	xxx	–	–	–
	Red oak (*Quercus ruba*)	xxx	–	–	–
Ulmaceae	Elm (*Ulmus americana*)	xx	xx	xx	–
Magnoliaceae	Tulip tree (*Liriodendron tulipfera*)	xxx	tr	tr	–
Rosaceae	Black cherry (*Prunus serotina*)	xxx	tr	–	–
Leguminoseae	Black locust (*Robinia pseudacacia*)	xxx	–	–	–
Aceracea	Striped maple (*Acer pennsylvanicum*)	xxx	tr	–	–
	Sugar maple (*Acer saccharinum*)	xxx	–	–	–
Rhamnaceae	Buckthorn (*Rhamnus cathartica*)	xxx	tr	tr	–
Tiliaceae	Basswood (*Tilia americana*)	xxx	x	x	–
Nyssaceae	Blackgum (*Nyssa sylvatica*)	xxx	tr	–	–
Oleaceae	White ash (*Fraxinus americana*)	xx	xx	xxx	tr

xxx = 10–25 percent sugar
xx = 2–10 percent sugar
x = 0.5–2 percent sugar

tr = trace < 0.5 percent sugar
– = 0.5–0 percent sugar
Nomenclature follows Gray's *Manual of Botany*, 8th ed., 1950.

No reducing sugars were found.

solution; (3) the turgor pressure must be positive in the direction of flow. Since the carbon-nitrogen relation of phloem exudate from trees is compatible with that of the tissues produced in growth, and because exudation continues for half an hour or more, Zimmermann assumes that the exudate represents a true sample of the assimilate stream and he recognizes from its volume that it must originate from sieve tubes quite removed from the cut.

Recognizing that Schumacher (1939) and Currier, Esau, and Cheadle (1955) have established the plasmolyzability of the functioning sieve tubes, Zimmermann approaches the permeability problem in a different way. Taking successive samples for periods up to 25 minutes, he found a steady dilution of the sieve-tube sap as a result of the release of the turgor pressure. This effect was discussed in detail by Crafts (1936, p. 75) and Cooil (1941). Zimmermann considers it as evidence for the semipermeable nature of the sieve-tube cytoplasm. Because the sieve-tube system retains its sugar content for a day or two after leaf fall in autumn, Zimmermann thinks that the sieve tubes do not leak, and hence must be semipermeable. Furthermore, because the sugar gradients are not related to molecular size, he considers that the molecules are removed metabolically, not by leakage.

Considering next the longitudinal permeability of the sieve tubes, Zimmermann points out that a second cut made a half hour to several weeks after the initial cut will restore flow. This indicates that the sieve tubes a short distance from the initial cut are not injured and that the sieve plates must be permeable in order to accommodate the volume flow that passes them. With Crafts (1938, 1951), Zimmermann accepts this evidence for longitudinal permeability of the sieve tubes. Although the evidence seems clear, we do not yet have any concept of how this permeability is established or maintained.

By collecting sieve-tube sap from different heights of the tree Zimmermann showed that there were concentration gradients of sugar in the phloem throughout the summer. When the leaves yellowed in the autumn the gradient of total sugars flattened but that of mannitol and sucrose remained positive; that of stachyose and raffinose became negative. Since the former two compounds predominate (0.274 M) compared with the latter (0.133 M), Zimmermann points out that the pressure-flow mechanism should continue to function with the stachyose and raffinose being moved against this concentration gradient. That this is true is borne out by the maintenance of flow after leaf fall. This observation parallels that of Bennett and Esau (1936) that curly-top virus of sugar beet moved into the seed coat of beet to an extremely high concentration against a virus gradient during food storage in the seed.

By studying diurnal fluctuation in the sucrose concentration of sieve-tube exudate Zimmermann (1958) showed that a concentration peak moves down the trunk at a rate of about 1.5 meters per hour. This should be a fairly accurate measure of the rate of flow of the assimilate stream at the time these collections were made.

In further experiments Zimmermann (1958) studied phloem exudation and exudate concentration from normal and defoliated ash trees. Defoliation caused a flattening in the total sugar gradient and a lowering of concentration of all the sugars present. The sieve tubes, however, remained turgid and exudate was collected during the period of new leaf growth. In autumn the sieve tubes could be tapped until two to three weeks after formation of the abscission layer. These observations indicate that sieve tubes do not leak but, rather, that removal of sugars must result from some metabolic process. After defoliation or abscission there is a rapid interconversion of stachyose to sucrose. Zimmermann suggests that an α-D-galactosidase located in the side-wall cytoplasm of the sieve tubes may remove D-galactose units as the oligosaccharides pass, producing raffinose from stachyose, and sucrose from raffinose; sucrose may then be removed. Sucrose removal is very rapid after defoliation but slows down and stops after 5 days; later it increases again.

From the breakdown rate of stachyose immediately following defoliation and the measured stachyose gradient along the trunk before defoliation Zimmermann calculated the rate of stachyose translocation as 63, 73, and 54 cm per hour for three defoliation experiments. The total molar gradient of the three sugars and D-mannitol, which make up about 90 percent of the dry weight of the sieve-tube sap, is positive in the downward direction during the whole summer. After defoliation this gradient disappears and some of the individual sugar gradients become negative. This is taken as evidence for turgor pressure being the driving force for translocation through the sieve tubes.

Much attention has been paid to the question of the longitudinal gradient of osmotically active substances in the phloem. The theory of Münch requires such a gradient with a return of water to the xylem as assimilates are condensed to nonosmotic substances in growth or storage. Such a separation of solute and solvent would require expenditure of much energy. The point usually missed in these considerations is that active cells in the sinks often require as much or more water in their growth as is associated with the osmotic substances, and so it seems logical that they should absorb the total assimilate stream without separation of solutes and solvent. Organs such as cucurbit fruits require more water than that obtained from the assimilate stream (Crafts and Lorenz, 1944b).

Ziegler (1956) studied the sugars in the sieve tubes by chromatography and found sucrose the sole sugar in 11 species. He found a negative gradient of phosphate in the sieve-tube sap of *Tilia, Acer, Robinia,* and *Quercus.* In 1958, working with the isolated vascular bundles of the petiole of *Heracleum,* he found that these bundles have a stronger respiration than ground parenchyma (3 times on the basis of protein N). Phloem and xylem were equally involved in this and both have the same respiratory quotient. Consumption of O_2 by the xylem was almost completely stopped, that by the phloem severely checked, and that by the petiole parenchyma unaffected by cyanide treatment. Since in all these tissues the succinic acid oxidase was active, Ziegler concludes that some other terminal oxidase system must be functioning. In isolated bundles or separated phloem and xylem strands O_2 consumption was not influenced by general or by one-sided application of sugar or fluorescein. Isolated phloem strands transport C^{14}-labeled sucrose and K fluorescein equally rapidly and in no case faster than killed tissue. Ziegler concludes that energy expenditure is required for all transport mechanisms and that they cannot be discriminated on the basis of their energy demands. He considers his results as providing evidence for a mass-flow mechanism.

Weatherley *et al.* (1959), using the willow aphid method of Kennedy and Mittler, studied the rate of flow and chemical composition of sieve-tube sap from *Salix viminalis.* The normal rate of exudation was around 1 mm^3 per hour. Since the average length of sieve-tube elements in this species is 170μ and the diameter 23μ, they could calculate the linear rate of movement. This turned out to be 100 cm per hour, equivalent to the contents of 100 sieve-tube elements per minute. The sap contained between 5 and 15 percent sucrose, up to 0.4 percent raffinose, no reducing sugars, and about 0.5 percent amino acids. In senescent leaves the sugar in the exudate dropped to a mere trace and the amino acid content increased to as high as 5 percent.

Girdles placed some distance above and below exuding stylets failed to stop exudation, indicating a rapid sealing of the cut ends of the sieve tubes and a rapid switch-over in source of supply from the leaves to storage cells in the stem. Using isolated stem segments and irrigated strips of bark, they found that there was no evidence for polar movement of the sap, that a minimum length of about 16 cm of stem or around 800 to 1000 sieve elements in length was required to produce the full exudation rate, and that raising the DPD on the inside of the bark reduced the volume rate of exudation but increased its concentration. Exudation continued, indicating maintenance of turgor even when the DPD was increased to 20 atm or more. Secretion of sugar into the sieve tubes continued, though slowly, even against a sieve-tube concentration of 50 percent. Weatherley *et al.* consider that their work provides evidence supporting the mass-flow hypothesis.

Willenbrink (1957) studied the effect of several respiration inhibitors on the central bundles of petioles of *Pelargonium zonale*. Starting by measuring respiration on phloem versus whole petioles, he concluded that the vascular tissue has a respiration intensity several times higher than that of cortex parenchyma. Treatment of the phloem with N_2, H_2, or CO had no inhibiting effect on translocation. HCN blocked the transport of fluorescein, nitrogenous substances, phosphorus compounds, and labeled assimilates in a reversible fashion. When Willenbrink used 2,4-dinitrophenol, arsenite, azide, and iodo acetic acid, he obtained a complete and irreversible inhibition; fluoride gave only a weak response. His conclusion was that translocation in the phloem is dependent upon the process of respiration. He considered that the different responses to different inhibitors by fluorescein, nitrogen compounds, and phosphorus compounds indicate independent movement.

chapter eight

Movement of Radioactive Indicators

The introduction of C^{14}-labeled compounds made available ideal indicators for translocation studies, for experiments have proved that many such compounds may be absorbed from the surface of treated leaves and translocated to roots or shoots or both, and their location determined by freeze drying and autoradiography. Thus translocation studies may be made on intact plants, and by stopping all physiological activity by freeze drying at different times and under different experimental conditions, uptake rates, transport rates, and distribution patterns may be determined.

Fang *et al.* (1951) showed that C^{14}-labeled 2,4-D is rapidly absorbed and moved in bean plants. Young plants absorbed and moved the indicator more rapidly than old ones; absorption and translocation were not correlated with dosage applied; and small amounts of the growth regulator were broken down and metabolized with a constant loss of radioactive CO_2. Studying absorption and translocation of 2,4-dichloro, 5-iodo phenoxy acetic acid containing radioactive iodine by oats, wheat, corn beans, sunflowers, dandelion, and plantain, Gallup and Gustafson (1952) found the monocots to absorb the indicator more slowly than dicots. Translocation was also less rapid in monocots, and the authors postulated a block in the intercalary region. This turns out to be a physiological barrier rather than an anatomical one (Crafts and Yamaguchi, 1958).

O'Kelley (1953) showed that $C^{14}O_2$ applied to leaves of a cotton plant is absorbed; the C^{14} moved into the boll and was laid down in the cotton fiber. Indications were that cellulose synthesis occurred throughout the length of the fiber and, hence, that growth was taking place throughout its length. Rabideau and Mericle (1953) applied $C^{14}O_2$ to young corn plants and found accumulation to take place in the growing shoot and root tips. In histoautoradiographs of roots, the vascular bundles could be followed down into the meristematic region. Hanson and Biddulph (1953), using radioactive phosphorus and rubidium, demonstrated a diurnal variation in the portions of absorbed tracers translocated by shoots of bean; maximum movement occurred during the day. Low-salt, high-sugar roots transported the greater amounts to shoots.

Rediske and Biddulph (1953) used radioactive iron (Fe^{55}) for studies on the absorption and translocation of iron by roots of bean. The best translocation occurred when the plants were grown in a solution containing very low phosphorus and no iron, maintained at pH 4.0. Poorest translocation occurred when the plants were given high phosphorus and high iron and maintained at pH 7.0. When the iron was injected into the primary leaves of bean, it failed to move out to the younger leaves under conditions of high pH and high phosphorus.

Rediske and Selders (1953) studied the uptake and movement of strontium-90 by bean plants grown in culture solution. Absorption of Sr^{90} was proportional to concentration in the nutrient solution up to 100 ppm; accumulation on the roots decreased as acidity was increased from pH 7.0 to pH 4.0; the ratio of translocated Sr^{90} to root Sr^{90} increased in the same way. There was no redistribution of Sr^{90} within the leaf system at pH 6.0. Fang and Butts (1954a), studying labeled 2,4-D in corn and wheat plants, found absorption and translocation by these monocots slower than in bean. Like Gallup and Gustafson they postulated a block at the intercalary meristem. They found two unknown compounds containing C^{14} resulting from the breakdown of 2,4-D, which they took to indicate detoxification.

When excised tops of *Sedum spectabile* plants were exposed in a photosynthesis chamber to $C^{14}O_2$, the following compounds were identified by chromatography from the tissues: fructose, glucose, sucrose, malic acid, citric acid, and sedoheptulose. Sedoheptulose, glucose, fructose, and sucrose were found in the water in which the plants were standing; Tolbert and Zill (1954) concluded that they were translocated down the stalks during the treatment.

Weibe and Kramer (1954) used P^{32}, Rb^{86}, I^{131}, S^{35}, Ca^{45}, and Sr^{90} to study the uptake and movement of minerals by barley roots. They found that although the tips absorbed the various ions freely, very little upward translocation if any took place 5 mm from the tip. Greatest translocation occurred from the region 30 mm back of the root tip. Translocation from the region 50 mm or more behind the tip was less than from 30 mm but greater than from the tip. Upward transport of Ca^{45} and Sr^{90} was very limited. All isotopes moved toward the tips of the roots; P^{32} and S^{35} accumulated there. Steam ringing reduced both upward and downward movement of P^{32} whether the ring was above or below the point of uptake. Table 8-1 presents data on P^{32}, Rb^{96}, I^{131}, and S^{35}.

Table 8-1

Translocation of Radioisotopes by Barley Roots

Distance of application from root tip	Percent of isotope translocated upward			
	P^{32}	Rb^{86}	I^{131}	S^{35}
0–4 mm	1.3	4.2	1.0	1.7
7–10 mm	8.5	14.3	28.3	5.2
27–30 mm	34.4	14.7	28.9	11.8
57–60 mm	24.9	9.4	22.7	9.2

Fang and Butts (1954b) found that 2,4-D treatment greatly reduced the upward movement of P^{32} to leaves of bean, the degree of reduction being proportional to the amount of 2,4-D supplied. Aronoff (1955) used $C^{14}O_2$ applied to limited areas of soybean leaves to study translocation of the labeled sugar. He found that under normal conditions movement was greatest to the growing regions. Little or no movement laterally to adjacent portions of the leaf occurred. Sugar would not flow out of the cut petiole into water but translocation was resumed if and when roots were formed. Steam ringing of the petiole prevented export. Steaming below a leaf node did not prevent acropetal transport to younger leaves.

Kendall (1955) attempted to study the effect of certain metabolic inhibitors on the export of P^{32} from bean leaves. The inhibitors were injected into the hollow petioles one hour after application of a 10μl droplet of P^{32} near the center of the leaf. Translocation of the P^{32} was inhibited by dinitro phenol, fluoroacetate, 2,4-D, IAA, or TIBA. Kendall adjusted his P^{32} solution to pH 1.5 and within 1 to 2 hours noted necrotic spots where the application had been made. As shown by Crafts (1956a), however, a pH below 2.0 is too acid for treatments aimed at supplying tracers for translocation, because the initial contact of the solution injures the phloem and hinders transport. Wright and Barton (1955) studied the role of transpiration in uptake and distribution of P^{32} in sunflower plants. They found greatest uptake from culture solution of low osmotic pressure with plants in the light and 59 percent relative humidity. Similar plants in the dark took up much less P^{32}; plants in the light and relative humidity of 95 percent absorbed even less; plants in culture solution of high osmotic pressure, light, and 59 percent relative humidity took up more than the previous two but less than the first. Of the first two plants, the one in the light had a high concentration of P^{32} in the young top leaves whereas the plant in the dark had its highest concentration in the basal leaves. This effect the authors attribute to the relative rates of flow of the transpiration stream in the two plants. On the basis of several years experience in interpreting autoradiographs, the writer would attribute the difference to secondary movement of P^{32} from the lower leaves of the plant in the light, to upper leaves via the phloem. This would not occur without movement of assimilate resulting from photosynthesis.

Biddulph (1956) and Biddulph, Cory, and Biddulph (1956) using bean plants grown in culture solution, studied the absorption and translocation of S^{35} from the culture solution and from an injected leaf. Sulfur in the plants was determined by chemical analysis (for sulfur from the seed), by counting, and by autoradiography. They found a close correlation between dry matter and sulfur content throughout the nutrient range of 0.125 to 1.0 millimolar sulfur. Trifoliate leaves and roots were higher in sulfur than stems and primary leaves. A portion of sulfur in the plant remains mobile and moves freely from one organ to another. A portion of the seed sulfur originally moved to the roots is released for upward translocation only when sulfur is taken up from the culture solution by roots. The rate of downward movement of sulfur in the phloem of the stem is similar to that of phosphorus and sugar, and is greater than 40 cm per hour.

Rohrbaugh and Rice (1956) used C^{14}-labeled 2,4-D in studies on phosphorus nutrition of tomato plants. They found that phosphorus-deficient plants that were supplied with phosphorus as a complete nutrient solution 3 days before treatment with 2,4-D had greater stem curvature, lower fresh weight of tops, and more radioactivity in hypocotyls and roots than did plants that did not receive PO_4 until 24 hours after treatment. Plants receiving phosphate 8 hours before 2,4-D treatment were intermediate. Rohrbaugh and Rice concluded that 2,4-D is not readily translocated through tomato plants that are seriously deficient in phosphorus.

Zinc-65 was used by Wallihan and Heymann-Herschberg (1956) in studies on zinc distribution in citrus. Zinc deficiency is common in citrus, and a variety of application methods are used in attempts to correct it. The studies showed that young leaves absorbed and transported zinc more readily than old, and that more zinc was picked up from high concentrations (10 mg Zn^{65} per pot) than from low (0.7 mg Zn^{65} per pot). No differences were found between application to upper and lower leaf surfaces, nor was distribution different between application through the leaves and through the roots.

Hay and Thimann (1956), examining 2,4-D in bean plants by means of an analysis by bioassay, studied translocation out of a treated leaf. They found that transport, accompanied by extensive breakdown, ceased at about the middle of the hypocotyl, and none of the compound entered the roots. This finding is in distinct contrast to the results of Crafts (1956a), who was able to obtain complete infiltration of bean roots with radioactive 2,4-D, and of Clor (1951, reported in Crafts, 1956a), who found that, when applied to one cotton plant growing in a culture solution, 2,4-D leaked from the roots into a second plant in the same culture jar and produced its typical symptoms in young leaves. Hay and Thimann found transport proportional to amount applied up to 75 μg per plant. Transport was completely inhibited by ringing and by dark treatment; it could be induced in the dark, however, by applying sugar. Sucrose did not increase transport in the light or at 4° C. Neither mannitol, arabinose, nor urea could substitute for sucrose. Hay and Thimann deduced that 2,4-D transport is not brought about by simple osmotic forces, but involves a metabolic component.

Crafts (1956a, b) reported 3 years work with C^{14}-labeled 2,4-D (carboxy labeled) on bean, cotton, cucumber, and wild morning glory (*Convolvus arvensis*). Quick killing with dry ice followed by drying between hot, dry blotters proved to introduce an artifact, in that the tracer was absorbed and translocated in the xylem to regions where drying was most rapid. This artifact was eliminated by freeze drying.

The studies showed that 2,4-D was absorbed and translocated into bean roots in around 3 hours; bending of hypocotyls took place in 2 to 3 hours; movement into terminal buds required 6 hours; after 24 hours, intensity of radiation in autographs decreased in roots and treated leaves. These rates were taken to result from metabolism of the 2,4-D as shown by Weintraub *et al.* (1952). Application of the droplet over the midrib near the leaf base was the most favorable location; surfactant enhanced absorption; in large plants absorption and translocation were greatest from the primary leaves, less from successively higher ones. Translocation took place in plants that were under water stress, so that bending did not occur.

Translocation into stems and roots of cotton and cucumber plants was greatest from cotyledons, less from successively higher leaves. No transport took place from very young leaves that were still importing foods from more mature leaves. The conclusion was that 2,4-D was diffusing into the leaves, entering the symplast, migrating to the phloem, and moving along in the assimilate stream with food materials.

Similar conclusions followed the work with wild morning glory but with this species, a perennial weed, point of application proved very important. The tracer would not move out of young expanding tip leaves; it moved readily from median or basal leaves; movement to roots was greatest from basal leaves; movement to growing stem tips, flowers, and fruits took place from any mature leaves. Two-way movement from median leaves was evident in many plants and often many intervening leaves, between the treated leaf and the growing tip, were by-passed.

Stage of growth was also important. In old established plants in the field early season treatment on young succulent shoots failed to produce movement; at the bud stage transport was predominately downward; at flowering and fruiting it was into the flowers and fruits; in the ripe seed stage it was predominately downward again. A large number of plants treated in the field produced results indicating the importance of treatment time. After 4 hours movement was 11 inches; after 27 hours, 30 inches; after 48 hours, 39 inches; in 8 days, to the full depth of excavation—that is, 6 feet. Treatments were mostly by droplet application of 2,4-D acid in 50 percent alcohol with a surfactant. In one field test radioactive 2,4-D acid was added to an emulsifiable acid formulation of 2,4-D in sufficient quantity to produce autoradiographs.

Leonard and Crafts (1956) studied the uptake and distribution of labeled 2,4-D in seven woody plants that are pests on California ranges. In coyote brush (*Baccharis pilularis*) 2,4-D was absorbed and translocated slightly in February, intensely in April, less in May and June, and not at all in July. In February and March its movement was downward from treated leaves, in April almost entirely upward. In arroyo willow (*Salix lasiolepis*) little translocation occurred before April 15; from late April until autumn, transport was continuous, movement being both upward and downward. By October all movement was downward.

In wedge-leaf ceanothus (*Ceanothus cuneatus*) little translocation of 2,4-D occurred under the experimental conditions. There was serious contact burn from the 2,4-D, which probably injured the phloem and prevented transport. In manzanita (*Arctostaphylos manzanita*) 2,4-D was absorbed and translocated, mostly upward in March, downward in May. In toyon (*Photinia arbutifolia*) uptake was prominent from February through October; transport was primarily downward in February and March, upward from May through July, downward in autumn.

Tracer studies failed for the most part in blue oak (*Quercus douglasii*). The leaves of this species are tender and the treatments caused severe contact injury. In live oak (*Quercus wislizenii*) 2,4-D moved actively from February through September. Movement was entirely downward in February, upward after new growth started in March, but largely downward through the summer.

These studies have had several results: (1) They emphasize the deleterious effects of contact injury in the use of toxic tracers; (2) They strengthen the evidence for correlation between food movement and 2,4-D movement in plants; (3) They show that the tracer may move for many months in evergreen species but only for short periods in deciduous plants; and (4) They show the important relations of growth conditions and the interaction of environmental factors in determining where and under what conditions foods move in plants.

Nelson and Gorham (1957) studied the uptake and movement of C^{14}-labeled glucose and sucrose and C^{14}-labeled photosynthate in soybean seedlings. Very little of the labeled sugars was absorbed by leaves, and this only when surfactant was included in the solution applied. Boron plus surfactant in the applied solution increased absorption so that there was some export from the treated leaves. Presence of significant amounts of the labeled sugars in the opposite leaves, however, poses the question of how their samples were taken. In carefully freeze-dried plants such amounts are not usually found. Furthermore, the greater export in the dark than in the light is difficult to understand in terms of normal translocation.

C^{14}-labeled photosynthate spread throughout the plants studied by Nelson and Gorham in 3 hours. In the light more C^{14} was found in the shoot tip than in the root; in the dark the reverse was true. In a recent note Nelson *et al.* (1958) report translocation of C^{14} from $C^{14}O_2$-treated leaves at amazing velocities to stem tips, mature trifoliate leaves, opposite primary leaves, and stems. The velocity of flow was "at least twenty times greater than that reported for sugars." Again, however, the methods come into question. Since the $C^{14}O_2$ was injected into a closed polyethylene bag containing the leaf, it seems perfectly possible that movement took place in the gaseous phase through the intercellular space system of the plant. Rice and Rohrbaugh (1953) found that 2,4-D ester dissolved in kerosene moved from leaves to roots of destarched bean plants via the intercellular space system.

Barrier and Loomis (1957) studied the absorption and translocation of 2,4-D and P^{32} by leaves of soybean and sugar beet. They found the absorption of 2,4-D to be increased by surfactants and increased temperature; neither of these responses was found with P^{32}. Absorption of 2,4-D by roots of soybean was not accelerated by an increase in temperature from 13° C to 23° C. P^{32} when applied to one leaf of a soybean seedling, followed in 2 hours by washing and left for one week to be distributed, was found in all younger leaves, in the stem, and in roots. Older leaves were by-passed. Absorption of 2,4-D and P^{32} was not reduced by depletion of leaf carbohydrate; translocation was reduced or stopped. Because the Q_{10} for translocation was of the order of 2 the authors proposed that a chemical reaction is involved. However, until the Q_{10} for movement of endogenous sugars by these plants is determined it seems uncertain that such a reaction is the only plausible explanation. Analyses of treated leaves showed that after 24 hours 80 percent of the absorbed P^{32} was in an organic form. Six hours after beet leaves were treated with P^{32} autoradiographs showed that the tracer was localized in high concentration in the veins.

Romney and Toth (1957), studying the distribution of Mn^{54}, found this element, when absorbed by roots, to concentrate in mature rather than in young leaves. In alfalfa leaves the Mn^{54} concentrated in the tips of leaves; in soybean and tomato it was localized in interveinal tissue in small islands. Foliar absorption of Mn^{54} resulted in movement and accumulation in meristems. After 10 days it was present throughout the plants. There was a distinct antagonism between cobalt and manganese.

Tests on the relative mobility of 15 inorganic elements in bean plants have been conducted by Bukovac and Wittwer (1957). Applications were made by measured droplets and by leaf dipping. Uptake and movement were measured on the droplet-treated plants by cutting out the treated spot and (1) fractionating into treated leaf, untreated leaf and stem, and roots, and counting the isotopes; (2) autoradiographing. The different isotopes were found to move by different tissue systems (some via phloem, others via xylem) and absorption rates proved to vary widely. Although the different treatment solutions could not be standardized with respect to specific activity, the results of this test are extremely interesting. It is important at this stage of the work with labeled tracers to understand the inherent differences in their reactions in plants. Table 8-2 presents the classification of the tracers studied by Bukovac and Wittwer.

Table 8-2

Classification of Elements as to their Mobility in Bean Plants

Mobile		Partially mobile		Immobile	
isotope	chemical form	isotope	chemical form	isotope	chemical form
Rb^{86}	$RbCl_2$	Zn^{65}	$ZnCl_2$	Ca^{45}	$CaCl_2$
Na^{22}	$NaCl$	Cu^{64}	$Cu(NO_3)_2$	Sr^{89}	$SrCl_2$
K^{42}	K_2CO_3	$Mn^{52\text{-}54}$	$MnCl_2$	$BaLa^{140}$	$BaCl_2$
P^{32}	H_3PO_4	$Fe^{55\text{-}59}$	$FeCl_3$	Mg^{28}	
Cl^{36}	HCl	Mo^{99}	$(NH^4)_2MoO_4$		
S^{35}	SO_4				

Bukovac and Wittwer interpret the variable rates of uptake and movement of these various isotopes as making transport by a mass-flow mechanism unlikely. However, as will be discussed (Crafts and

Yamaguchi, 1958; Crafts, 1959), the movement of a number of labeled organic tracers has been found to correlate with their relative mobility in parenchyma and hence with their supply to the phloem. It seems possible in this case also that the movement of these tracers in the phloem may be fairly uniform but that the ultimate distribution may be determined by the following: absorption and presentation into the phloem, different degrees of uptake out of the phloem by phloem parenchyma, and possible differences in the rate at which the tracers pass the sieve plates while being carried in a common stream.

Koontz and Biddulph (1957) made some important studies on the absorption and translocation of P^{32} in bean plants. The plants were grown in one-half Hoagland's solution in light chambers with 1000 foot-candles fluorescent illumination, temperature of 24° C ± 1, and 60 percent ± 4 relative humidity. Different phosphorus salts were used, and wetting agents, application methods, effects of cation and pH, the time course of uptake, age and position of sprayed leaf, and effect of repeated application were investigated. The spray application proved superior to vein injection and droplet application; the amount of P^{32} translocated increased with increased dosage and was independent of leaf area; old leaves transported the most P^{32}; younger leaves transported less; young expanding leaves exported none. Translocation decreased through the following series: $NaH_2PO_4 > K_2HPO_4 > K_3PO_4, > Na_2HPO_4, > NH_4H_2PO_4, > (NH_4)_2HPO_4 > H_3PO_4$ (injury) $> KH_2PO_4, > Na_3PO_4$. The amount of P^{32} translocated from a given compound seemed related to the persistence of solution on the leaf. Glycerin increased transport from KH_2PO_4 but reduced it from K_2HPO_4, probably because of complexing. Absorption fell off markedly after 30 hours but 60 percent was absorbed and 34.5 percent translocated after 96 hours. The amount of P^{32} moved downward in the stem was initially greater than that moved upward but after 48 hours accumulation in the upper part was greater than in the lower. Probably secondary movement in the transpiration stream was involved. Wetting agents failed to improve translocation in these tests.

Linder, Craig, and Walton (1957) found that tagged α-methoxy phenylacetic acid (MOPA), a growth-modifying compound, is translocated from primary leaves of bean into the roots whence it is exuded into the culture medium. The rate of exudation and reabsorption was determined by measuring radioactivity in the tap water surrounding roots of plants. Fig. 8-1 shows one such example.

The amount of MOPA exuded by roots was proportional to the amount applied to the leaves. Exudation of MOPA was retarded by removal of the lower half of the root system. Maintaining a concentration of MOPA in the culture medium around the roots (30 μg in 150 ml) did not prevent exudation of radioactive MOPA from roots. Lowering the oxygen supply around the roots did reduce

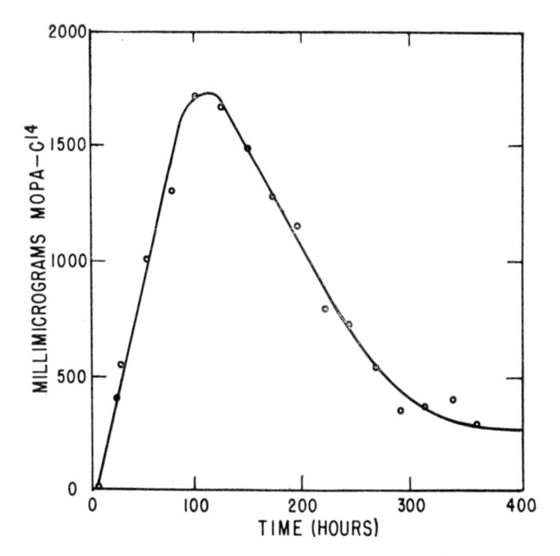

Fig. 8-1. Average amounts of MOPA-C^{14} detected in tap water surrounding the roots of bean following application to leaves.

exudation. These results fit a pattern involving absorption by the leaves, translocation with foods in the phloem, and secretion from the young active roots. A like behavior is shown by 2,4-D (Clor, 1951).

Biddulph and Cory (1957) have made critical studies on the comparative movement of tritiated water and P^{32}- and C^{14}-labeled photosynthate in bean plants. They point out the difficulties of getting critical evidence on the comparative transport of several tracers moving simultaneously. They applied P^{32} in the form of $NaH_2P^{32}O_4$ dissolved in tritiated water (THO). This solution was sprayed on the lower surface of the terminal leaflet of the first trifoliate leaf; $C^{14}O_2$ was confined on the upper surface. Translocation times were 15, 20, and 30 minutes. The plants were growing in one-half Hoagland's solution in a chamber at 23° C ± 1, with fluorescent lights providing 1000 to 1200 foot-candles, and a relative humidity of 60 percent ± 5. They were on a 12-hour day. The plants were divided into roots and stem to the node of the treated leaf. The stem was cut into 1-inch segments, usually 6 in number. These were analyzed separately, THO by distillation under reduced pressure, reduction, and counting of the tritium; P^{32} and C^{14} by counting.

The three tracers moved from the leaf down the stem at the following rates: P^{32} 86.5, THO 86.5, and C^{14} 107 cm per hour, respectively, including time for movement to the phloem. These rates of movement are comparable with many that have been measured. The authors discuss their results in relation to the postulated mechanisms of phloem transport and conclude that there is no basis in their work for abandoning the concept of pressure flow to explain movement within the stem via mature phloem.

The distribution of P^{32} and C^{14} simultaneously applied between phloem and xylem was determined at the end of a 60-minute migration period. The xylem contained 23.6 percent of the total translocated P^{32} and 24.4 percent of the total migratory C^{14}. These values were determined on the first 2 inches below the treated leaf but the same relation held throughout the lower portion of the stem. At the close of a 20-minute migration period in the first inch below the node, the xylem had 31 percent of the migratory THO, in the second inch 0.6 percent, and in the third inch none; tritiated water was present in the phloem throughout.

Biddulph and Cory interpret these results as indicating that the lateral membranes of the sieve-tube protoplasts are readily penetrated by sucrose, phosphate, and water. The same type of loss was present in the P^{32} and S^{35} microautoradiographs of S. Biddulph (Biddulph, 1956). If one is willing to accept the symplast concept, it seems much more logical to interpret this process as normal distribution via the mesoplasm of the interconnected sieve-tube—phloem-parenchyma—ray system. Many workers seem to fail to appreciate the function of the phloem as a distribution system. When the phloem is so considered, it is normal that solutes should enter the sieve tubes in the region of the source and leave them in the sinks without having to "leak" from the conduits across permeability barriers. Many studies have proved that the sieve tubes are copiously connected by plasmodesmata with companion cells and phloem parenchyma, and movement along the mesoplasm cores of these should take place readily with little resistance. If solutes can move across sieve plates as rapidly as we know they must, there should be little resistance to their movement laterally to adjacent living cells. After all, the whole sink for assimilate movement is ultimately made up of such parenchyma cells, and movement into them constitutes the terminal function of the distribution system. Lateral movement from the phloem along the stem is as normal as is movement into the meristems of root and shoot that are ordinarily recognized as major sinks.

In the above experiments Biddulph and Cory found the amount moving per unit applied was greatest for C^{14}, least for THO. The C^{14} moved largely as sucrose; the P^{32} as phosphate, or fructose-1,6-diphosphate free of the C^{14} label. The estimated total downward export per plant per day for C^{14} sucrose, THO, and P^{32} was 1.0 mg, 0.24 μl, and 1.0 μg, respectively. The ratio of C^{14} sucrose to THO was approximately 12 molal but an undetermined amount of unlabeled water was undoubtedly also translocated. There was an approximately linear relation between the logarithm of the P^{32} and C^{14} concentration and the distance from the point of entry into the stem.

Although Biddulph and Cory were unwilling to commit themselves as to the significance of their results with respect to mechanism, it seems to the writer that they have obtained almost irrefutable evidence for a pressure flow system in the bean. For the first time, except in the unnatural process of phloem exudation, we have positive evidence that the water and solutes move en masse through the sieve tubes. The small discrepancy in comparative rates of linear movement is no argument against this conclusion because, as has been pointed out many times, the differential entry and exit of molecules into and out of the phloem is simply a necessary corollary to the function of this tissue. These processes must take place in a distribution system. Furthermore, the periodical passage through sieve plates must result in differential retardation of molecules, and the possibility of exchange of THO with H_2O along the route must change the relative amounts of solvent in the system. In the eyes of the writer this work by Biddulph and Cory is one of the most critical and hence valuable contributions that has been made to date in the field.

Kessler and Moscicki (1958) have shown that the well-known growth inhibitor TIBA has a marked influence on the transport of Ca^{45} in apple and tomato. Theirs is reminiscent of the work of Bukovac *et al.* (1956), who showed that anesthetization of bean with diethyl ether induced transport of Ca^{45} into the lower portions of the plant. In view of the experience with the artifact of xylem transport found in early work with C^{14}-labeled 2,4-D (Pallas and Crafts, 1957; Crafts, 1956a), it seems possible that these two responses may result from uptake and movement of the Ca^{45} solution by reversal of the transpiration stream. Only careful reinvestigation can provide an answer to this problem.

The attempt by Horowitz (1958) at mathematical treatment of the translocation problem emphasizes some of its difficulties. An analysis of the function of the sieve tubes—living cells buried deep in the parenchyma of the stem, surrounded by active living cells that are joined to these tubes by protoplasmic connections—seems almost hopeless. The very nature of the distribution function of this system seems to preclude the possibility of the control that is essential to mathematical treatment. Apparently the mass-flow mechanism is the only one that offers any hope for such analysis.

Biddulph *et al.* (1958) studied the circulation patterns of P^{32}, S^{35}, and Ca^{45} and found each of these elements to display a unique pattern of movement. Calcium, being under their conditions quite immobile, formed the basis for contrasting mobility of P^{32} and S^{35}. Sulfur remained mobile and underwent considerable redistribution whereas P^{32} remained very mobile and redistributed freely. During the course of growth of each succeeding leaf of bean, phosphorus is delivered directly to the growing leaf via the phloem. At maturity, on the other hand, the transpiration stream is the sole source of supply. All leaves export phosphorus to the shoot apex but they export to the root in amounts proportional to the proximity of the leaf to the root. During its course of downward movement there is significant lateral movement of phosphorus to the xylem; this material is then available for reascension of the stem. A circulation pattern for phosphorus is thus indicated.

With S^{35} there was found a preferential delivery to the young leaves; the older leaves were bypassed. The explanation probably lies mainly in a failure of retention in the older leaves, which allows for movement to the younger foliage via both phloem and xylem.

Ca^{45} entered the roots and moved into the leaves in the transpiration stream. In this experimental work there was no evidence for its redistribution.

Rice and Rohrbaugh (1958) studied the effect of potassium nutrition on movement of labeled 2,4-D in tomato. They found that if potassium-deficient plants were supplied with the nutrient before or at the same time that the 2,4-D was applied, greater stem curvature, greater growth inhibition, and greater movement of the labeled tracers occurred than occurred if the potassium were supplied 24 hours after. Apparently translocation of 2,4-D is markedly affected by the level of potassium in the plants.

Perkins, Nelson, and Gorham (1959) used autoradiography and counting to study distribution of C^{14}-labeled photosynthate and C^{14}-labeled sucrose, glucose, and fructose in soybean plants. In tests having an experimental time period of 5 to 10 minutes, the bulk of the C^{14} from photosynthate or from sugars introduced through a cut petiole was concentrated in and around the vascular tissues. These tissues were located on the same side of the stem as the petiole through which the C^{14}-labeled tracers had entered. The C^{14} of photosynthate was localized in the phloem; that of sucrose, introduced through the cut petiole, was concentrated in the xylem and the adjacent pith. The C^{14} of fructose and glucose was localized mainly in the xylem. The investigators concluded that all translocation need not take place in the phloem but that some may take place in the pith and xylem. It seems obvious that normal phloem transport may account for the observed presence of photosynthate in the phloem, and that xylem injection through a cut petiole may account for movement both upward and downward along the stem; the process by which movement might occur in the pith cells at a rate of 10 cm in 5 minutes, however, is not clear.

Nelson, Perkins, and Gorham (1959) studied translocation of C^{14}-labeled photosynthate in soybeans, using $C^{14}O_2$ applied either by injection into a polythene bag surrounding a leaf or by means of a lucite leaf chamber. In experiments lasting 10 minutes or longer, C^{14} was translocated out of the primary leaf downward toward the root along a pattern that decreased logarithmically; 70 percent of the C^{14} was present as sucrose. In 5-minute experiments a similar pattern of distribution was evident in the first four stem sections, but lower pieces of stem contained activity that did

Fig. 8-2. Movement of C^{14}-labeled 2,4-D (left), amitrol (center), and MH (right) from treated green leaves of *Tradescantia*. Treatment time, 48 hours; dosage, 0.5 μc per plant. Autoradiographs are at the top, mounted plants below. The pointers indicate the treated leaves.

not fall within the logarithmic pattern. In 35- or 18-second experiments small amounts of radioactivity were found in most parts of the stem and there was no regular pattern of distribution.

In culture-solution plants, radioactivity was found in root tips 42 cm from the treated primary leaf within 30 seconds of the introduction of the $C^{14}O_2$. This movement represents a linear velocity of 5040 cm per hour. The experimenters term this translation rapid as contrasted with normal phloem transport that took place at a velocity of 168 cm per hour. The rapid type of movement also took place across a steamed portion of a stem but not to the same extent as in a normal healthy stem. Since radioactivity was also found in the growing stem tips and trifoliate leaves of the steamed plants, the writers suggest that the tracer that moved downward through the xylem did not accumulate in the roots but was carried by the transpiration stream into the tops of the plants. This would have required that the C^{14} move in opposite directions through the xylem within the 30-second experimental period.

Fig. 8-3. Movement of C^{14}-labeled 2,4-D (left), amitrol (center), and MH (right) from treated chlorophyll-free leaves of *Tradescantia.* Treatment time, 48 hours; dosage, 0.167 μc applied to a single leaf.

In order to eliminate possible movement of $C^{14}O_2$ in the gaseous state in their plants, Nelson and his associates used lucite chambers for treating leaves at atmospheric pressure; the distribution was found to be the same as when the polythene bags were used. They then tried to distill $C^{14}O_2$ from stem sections of treated plants that were killed instantly in liquid nitrogen at the termination of the experimental period of 18 to 35 seconds. They found no radioactive CO_2 by this process. They believe that they have distinguished three distinct kinds of downward translocation in the soybean: (1) normal phloem transport at rates around 100 cm per hour, (2) rapid translocation in the xylem, and (3) rapid translocation in living cells. Translocation at a linear velocity of 3000 to 5000 cm per hour is defined by them as rapid. They consider that phloem transport may take place first in companion cells and not in sieve tubes.

The high-velocity flow, the writers suggest, cannot be a mass flow but rather a gaseous diffusion or movement at an interface.

They compare their fast movement to movement of the excitation stimulus in *Mimosa*.

Canny (1959) questions the conclusion of Nelson *et al.* (1959) that the rapid movement of C^{14} in their experiments is not in the gaseous phase and points out the permeable nature of polythene to CO_2. Nelson and his associates answer this criticism by describing their experiments with the lucite chamber. What they have not done, however, is to eliminate the possibility mentioned previously that $C^{14}O_2$ is moving to the roots via the intercellular space system. As mentioned by Crafts and Broyer (1938), with active photosynthesis going on in leaves and rapid growth taking place in roots, there may be a stream of almost pure O_2 moving by mass flow from leaves to roots. This might carry the $C^{14}O_2$ at the observed rates in the intercellular space system.

Using autoradiographic and counting technics the writer and his associates (Crafts and Yamaguchi, 1958; Crafts, 1958; Crafts and Foy, 1959; Crafts, 1959; and Crafts and Yamaguchi, 1960) have made studies on the comparative mobility of a number of C^{14}-labeled organic tracers. Earlier work on bean and morning glory had shown that the C^{14}-labeled 2,4-D would move readily from fully expanded leaves, but not from young growing leaves that were still importing foods. It was possible to demonstrate, with a variegated variety of *Tradescantia* that has some completely chlorotic shoots, that 2,4-D, amitrol (amino triazole), and MH (maleic hydrazide) will not move out of a chlorophyll-free leaf (Figs. 8-2 and 8-3) and that when applied to variegated leaves their extent of movement is correlated with the amount of green tissue in the treated leaf (Fig. 8-4). This is evidence that the synthesis and export of food are the motivating forces for the export of these labeled tracers from leaves.

Investigation had also indicated considerable variation among individual plants and individual experiments with respect to the extent of distribution of foliar-applied tracers into stems and roots. Experiments on the nutritional level of culture-solution grown *Zebrina* plants have shown that only in plants having active root growth is 2,4-D carried throughout the root system. Fig. 8-5 shows three *Zebrina* plants treated on an upper leaf with labeled 2,4-D. The one on the left had been growing for 30 days in tap water. The roots were large, but by the time of treatment growth had ceased. The plant in the center had been growing for 2 weeks in $\frac{1}{16}$ Hoagland's solution and the roots were active. The plant on the right

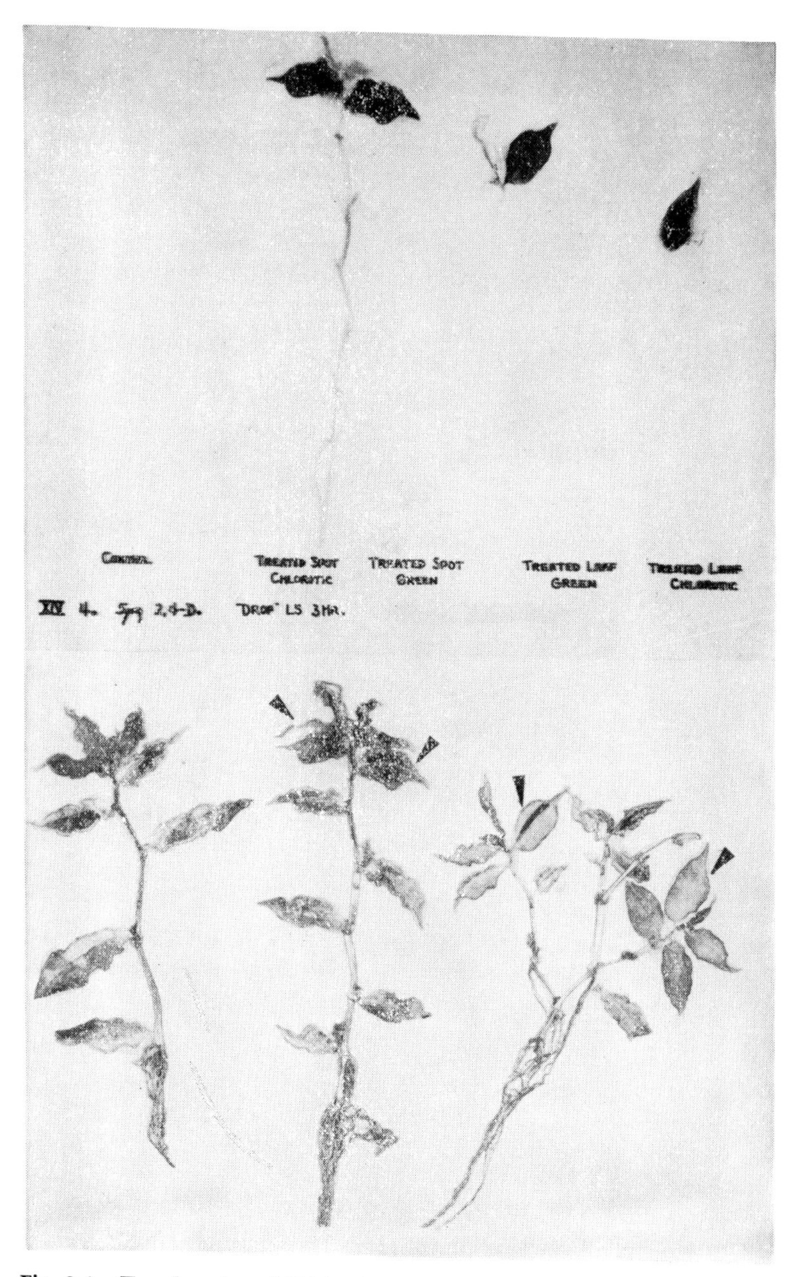

Fig. 8-4. Translocation of C^{14}-labeled 2,4-D from green and chlorotic leaves of *Tradescantia*. On the far right the completely chlorotic leaf shows movement only within the treated leaf. Movement from the other variegated leaves is roughly proportional to the amount of green tissue in them. Treatment time, 3 hours; dosage, 0.023 μc.

had exceptionally active roots; it received its 2,4-D treatment in two separate doses.

Two-way movement, previously demonstrated in morning glory, was very well illustrated when active sinks were created in growing tips and well-nourished roots of *Zebrina*. Fig. 8-6 (left) shows a plant that was prepared for the demonstration by having all but three basal leaves removed and two young growing leaves left at the tips.

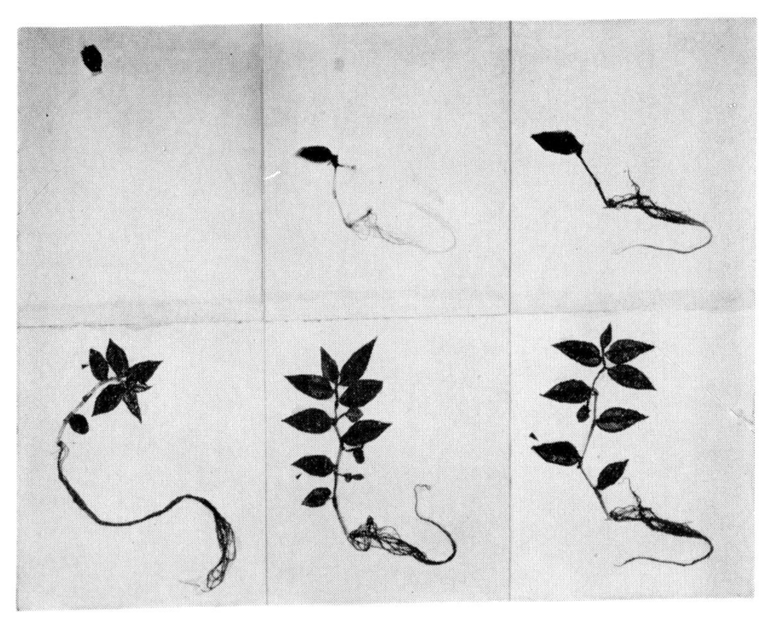

Fig. 8-5. Movement of C^{14}-labeled 2,4-D in *Zebrina* plants. Left, a plant held 30 days in tap water; center, a plant held 14 days in tap water; right, a plant continuously in culture solution. Treatment time, 4 days; dosage, 0.6 μc.

Labeled 2,4-D applied to two basal leaves moved both acropetally to the tip and basipetally into the roots. Fig. 8-6 (center and right) shows two plants manipulated to demonstrate the course of 2,4-D transport. Here the tracer was applied to two leaves at the tip of the stem of each plant. The growing points and all lower leaves were removed. In each plant the food stream carrying the 2,4-D moved basipetally in the stem and then split, some of the stream going out into the actively growing shoot, some to the roots.

In Fig. 8-6, a comparison of the plant on the left with the other two makes it evident that the indicator may be carried either in one direction or in two opposite directions within the stem as it is exported from a treated leaf. Note also that in all of these plants, leaves basal to the treated leaf or leaves are bypassed. These results cannot be explained on the basis of diffusional movement. They definitely indicate that the tracer is being carried in a stream and that it will not enter a leaf that is itself contributing to the volume of the stream—that is, a leaf that is exporting food.

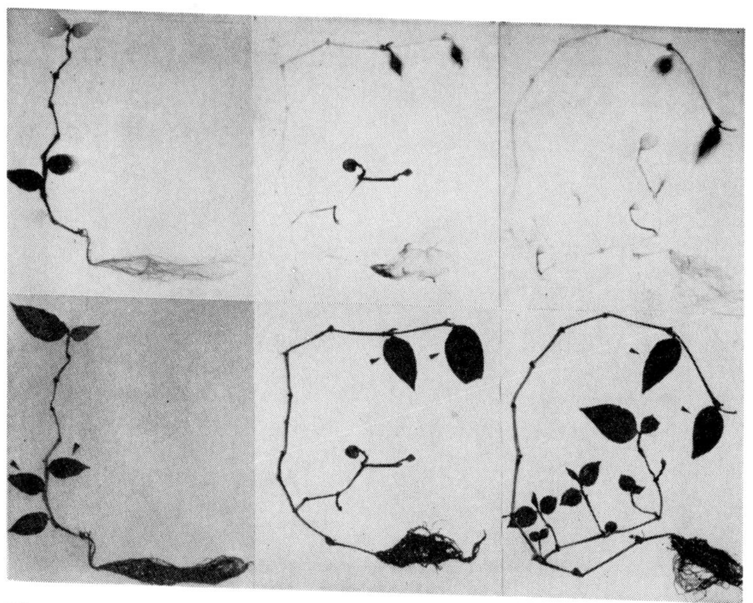

Fig. 8-6. Movement of C^{14}-labeled 2,4-D in plants manipulated to bring about two-way movement and basipetal movement. Treatment time, 9 days; dosage, 1.1 μc per plant.

Having determined the factors mainly responsible for the distribution of 2,4-D in plants it seemed desirable to distinguish between penetration and translocation of the tracer. It also seemed necessary to use other tracers in order to find if 2,4-D is a typical translocated solute for use in studies on distribution. In order to study absorption alone, a test was set up employing cubes of potato tuber tissue. The cubes were cut to a dimension of 1½ inches and placed on filter paper saturated with water in a metal container having a loose-fitting cardboard lid. Treatments were made to ¼-inch circles on top of the blocks, with lanolin rings to prevent

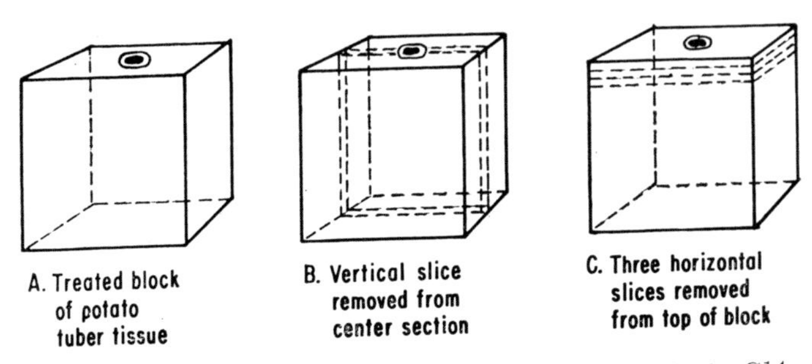

Fig. 8-7. Method of treating potato tuber blocks with six C^{14}-labeled compounds. Two blocks were treated with each tracer; one (B) was sliced vertically removing a 2-mm slice from the center; a second (C) had three 2-mm horizontal slices removed from the top.

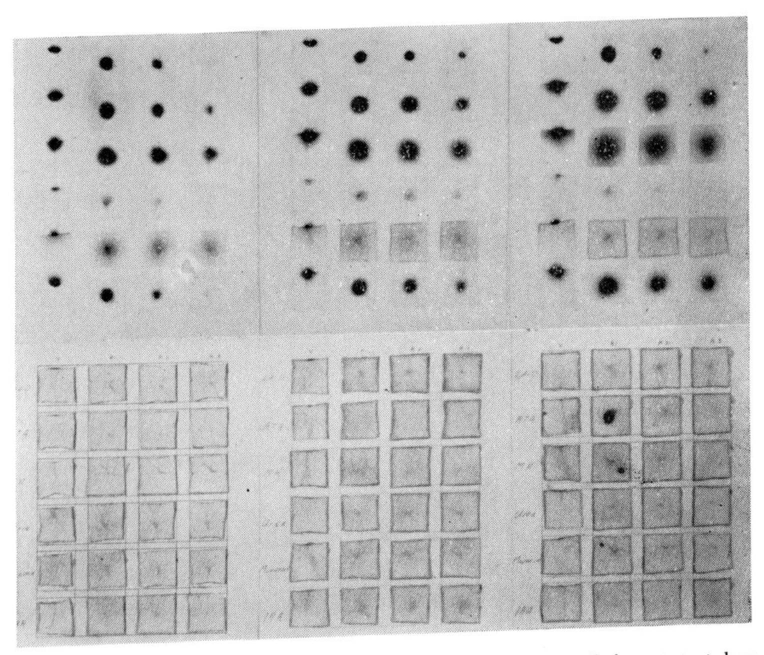

Fig. 8-8. Comparative mobility of six C^{14}-labeled compounds in potato tuber tissue. On the extreme left are shown the slices (below) and autoradiographs (above) of the vertically sliced blocks (Fig. 8-7B). Next to these and extending to the right are the three horizontal slices in order (2 mm, 4 mm, 6 mm). The chemicals from top to bottom: 2,4-D, amitrol, MH, urea, monuron, IAA. Treatment times: left, 2 days; center, 4 days; right, 8 days; dosage, 0.05 μc per treatment.

spreading. Treatment times were 2, 4, 8, and 16 days. Dosage was 0.05 μc per treatment with solutions having specific activities of 0.5 mc per mM. Six C^{14}-labeled tracers were used and each was applied to two tuber blocks (Fig. 8-7). At the end of the treatment time one block (Fig. 8-7B) was split vertically and a 2-mm slice through the center of the treatment area was taken. The second block (Fig. 8-7C) had three 2-mm horizontal slices cut from the top. The slices were freeze dried, mounted, pressed, and autographed by the usual method (Yamaguchi and Crafts, 1958). In mounting, the three horizontal slices were inverted so that the autographed faces represented the distribution of the tracers at levels of 2, 4, and 6 mm from the surface of the block.

Fig. 8-7 shows the method of sampling of the blocks; Fig. 8-8, the autographs. In the latter it can be seen from the depth of penetration and area of spread that 2,4-D, IAA, amitrol, and MH form a mobility series, with increasing movement in the order given. By following through the treatment time series it is evident that all of the material continued to move with time but that the initial mobility relation held for the 8 days. The 16-day autograph shows the same relation. Evidently 2,4-D is accumulated and retained within living cells and its movement in this relatively undifferentiated tissue is restricted. IAA moves a bit more freely, amitrol even more, and MH very freely. This is an interesting relation and it is substantiated by field results with the use of these chemicals in agriculture.

The remaining two chemicals show an interesting contrast in behavior. Urea is evidently hydrolyzed by urease and in this non-green tissue the label probably was lost as $C^{14}O_2$. Monuron, on the other hand, seems not to have entered the living cells but rather to have diffused along the cell walls and concentrated around the outside surface where evaporation was taking place.

To find the effects of this mobility relation on distribution of tracers in whole plants, 2,4-D, amitrol, and MH were applied to *Zebrina* plants that had been standing in the greenhouse without added nutrients. Fig. 8-9 shows the plants and autographs. The 2,4-D (left) has been retained in the three treated leaves and the adjacent stem. The amitrol (center) has moved to roots and shoot tips but has bypassed all mature leaves, an indication of free movement throughout the phloem. The MH (right) has not only moved throughout the phloem, and hence to roots and shoot tips, but can be seen in all intervening leaves. This indicates that it has migrated from phloem to xylem and moved along with the transpiration stream to all the leaves. Because the untreated leaves nearest to the treated ones are darker than those farther removed it seems that the transfer has occurred along the stem in relation to concentration

Fig. 8-9. Comparative movement of C^{14}-labeled 2,4-D, amitrol, and MH in *Zebrina.* Mobility of these three compounds increases in the above order (left to right). The plants were not growing rapidly but were alive and healthy. Treatment time, 4 days; dosage, 0.5 μc applied to the lower leaf surface.

in the phloem. Fig. 8-10 shows the same three tracers applied to leaves of barley plants growing with their roots on filter paper. Here amitrol moves as freely as MH.

Figs. 8-11 and 8-12 show barley plants and autographs from an experiment employing the six tracers used on the potato. Comparison of these with the response of potato tuber tissue shows that the extent of phloem movement is largely dependent upon the penetration of the tracers into the phloem. Chemicals like 2,4-D that are retained strongly by active living cells do not attain the general distribution shown by the more mobile ones such as MH. This would seem to imply that phloem transport was proceeding at least at a low velocity in all of these plants. Freely mobile chemicals such as MH attain wide distribution via phloem. At the same time, 2,4-D reaches the phloem in small quantities and these are reabsorbed by living cells along the phloem route so that movement in *Zebrina* was only for a short distance; in barley the tracer did not pass the active region of the intercalary meristem of the treated leaf.

In the green barley leaves the $C^{14}O_2$ from labeled urea is rapidly synthesized to sugars; these migrate to the phloem where

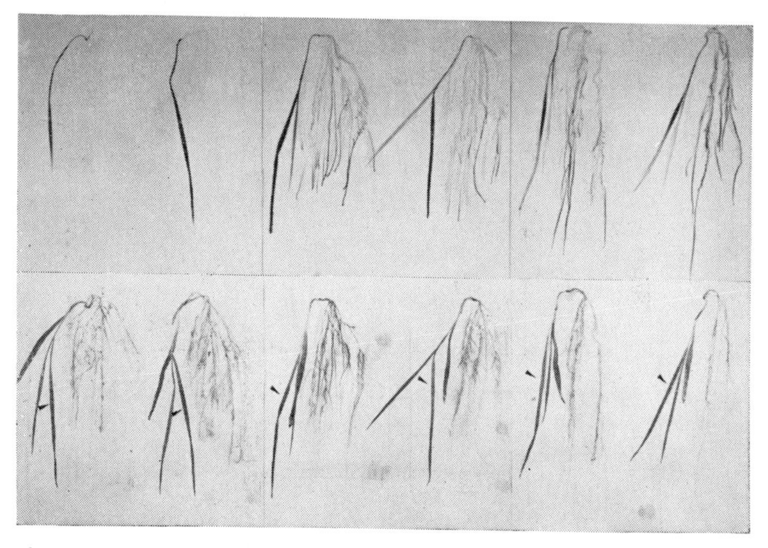

Fig. 8-10. Movement of C^{14}-labeled 2,4-D, amitrol, and MH (left to right) in barley plants actively growing with their roots spread on filter paper moistened by the culture solution. The labeled 2,4-D shows restricted movement; amitrol and MH became thoroughly distributed in these active plants. Treatment time, 2 days; dosage, 1 (left) and 4 (right) drops. Each drop of 10 μl contained 0.05 μc of activity.

they are transported readily to root and shoot tips and young growing leaves. Note that accumulation of the label occurs in meristematic regions of the crown and root tips. Monuron fails to leave the treated leaf. It seems unable to enter the phloem and move in the food stream. Its distribution seems to indicate that its migration occurs in the apoplast via the transpiration stream.

Fig. 8-13 shows four barley plants treated like those in Fig. 8-11 with dalapon at a dosage of 0.1 μc. Evidently this chemical moves freely in the phloem; it also seems to transfer freely and move in

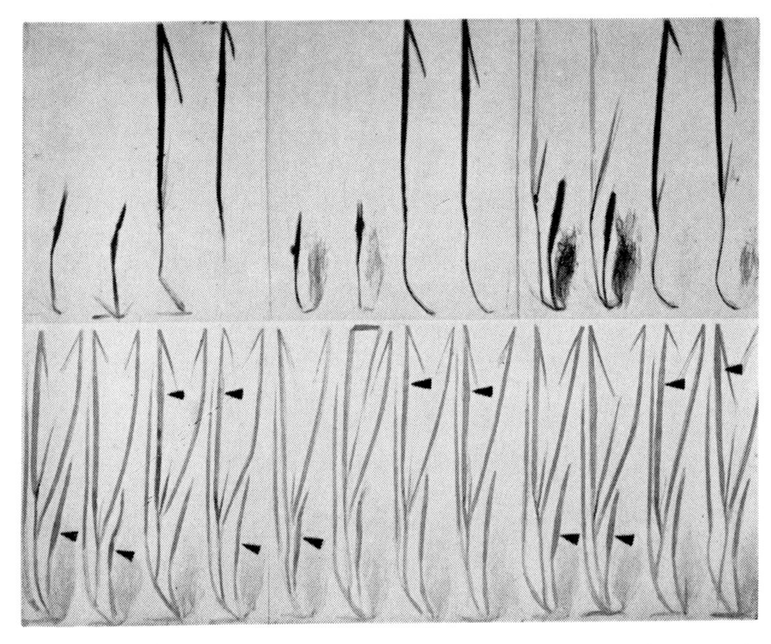

Fig. 8-11. Comparative movement of C^{14}-labeled 2,4-D (left), IAA (center), and amitrol (right) in barley. Each tracer was applied to 4 plants; 2 (left) were treated on leaf number 1, 2 (right) on leaf number 4. Treatment time, 1 day; dosage, 0.05 μc per plant applied in 10 μl of 50 percent alcohol with 0.1 percent Tween 20.

the transpiration stream; it seems not to accumulate in the roots to the high level shown by MH.

Labeled tracers have also been used in studies on the absorption of solutes by roots and their subsequent distribution in tops. When C^{14}-labeled 2,4-D was applied to barley, bean, cotton, and *Zebrina* plants via the culture solution at a rate of 1.25 μc in 250 ml for 10 days there was evidence that this compound is held in high concentration by roots. Very little of the labeled compound moved into the tops of barley, bean, and *Zebrina;* a fair quantity was translocated into cotton foliage (Crafts and Yamaguchi, 1960).

Excised barley root tips absorbed C^{14}-labeled 2,4-D from aerated Hoagland's solution to around 2.75 times the concentration in the culture solution in 30 minutes, but much of the absorbed tracer was released to the ambient solution during the subsequent 3½

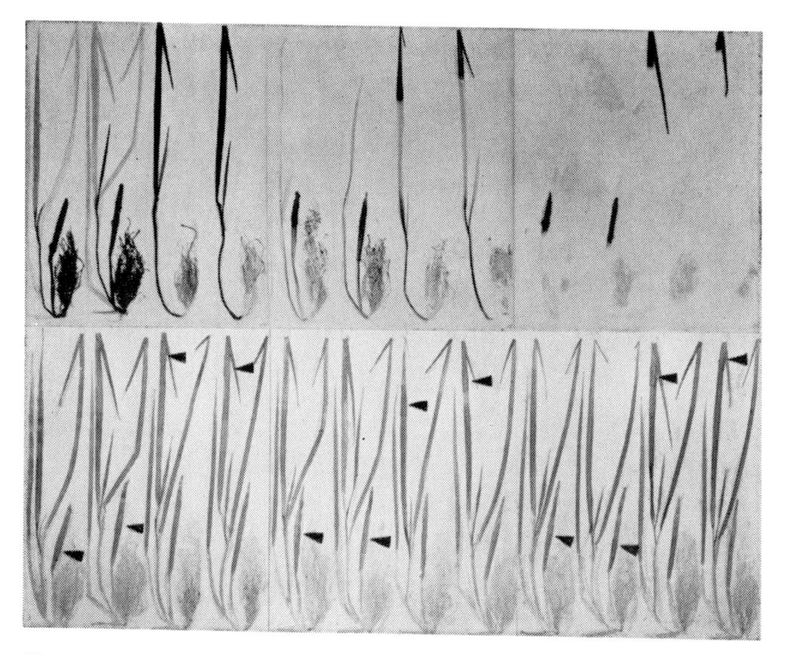

Fig. 8-12. Comparative movement of C^{14}-labeled MH (left), urea (center), and monuron (right). Treatments as in Fig. 8–11.

hours. Healthy roots aerated with air released more 2,4-D than did roots aerated with N_2.

Excised barley root tips that had accumulated C^{14}-labeled 2,4-D actively for 30 minutes released about 85 percent of the absorbed tracer in five 30-minute rinses in plain Hoagland's solution. When logarithms of the amounts released were plotted against log of time, and against log of amounts retained by the roots, straight-line relations were found. This indicates that the release of 2,4-D from roots is a desorption process.

Studies on the uptake of seven labeled compounds by roots of barley seedlings showed wide differences in the quantities of the different tracers transported to the tops. The compounds used were 2,4-D, amitrol, MH, urea, monuron, IAA, and dalapon. Plants were removed from the tracer solutions after 1, 2, 4, and 6 days, at which time the seedlings in amitrol were showing injury. Fig. 8-14 shows the plants and autoradiographs.

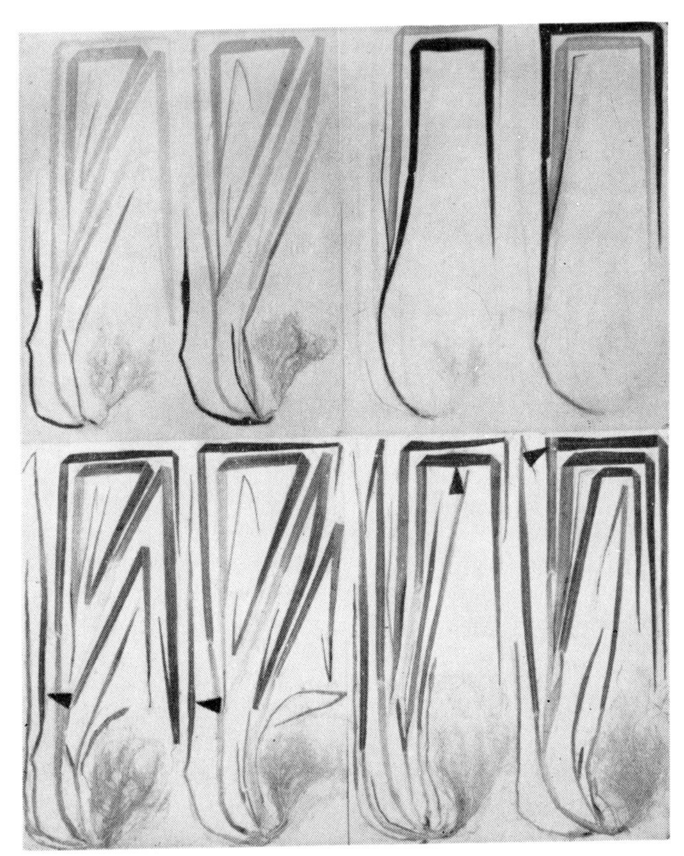

Fig. 8-13. Movement of C^{14}-labeled dalapon in barley. Treatment on leaf number 3 (left 2 plants) and leaf number 6 (right 2 plants). Treatment time, 1 day; dosage, 0.10 μc per plant.

Monuron and dalapon were moved into the leaves most rapidly; IAA and MH were next in order; 2,4-D and urea were still present in the leaves only in traces after 6 days.

When C^{14}-labeled 2,4-D, IAA, amitrol, MH, urea, dalapon, monuron, simazin, and P^{32} as phosphate were applied to roots of barley seedlings at a dosage rate of 0.0375 μc per 4 ml of culture solution per plant, 2,4-D, monuron, simazin, and IAA were absorbed sufficiently in 30 minutes to produce strong autographs of roots. Phosphate penetrated the roots more slowly but by 8 hours it had caught up with the above four compounds. After one day the

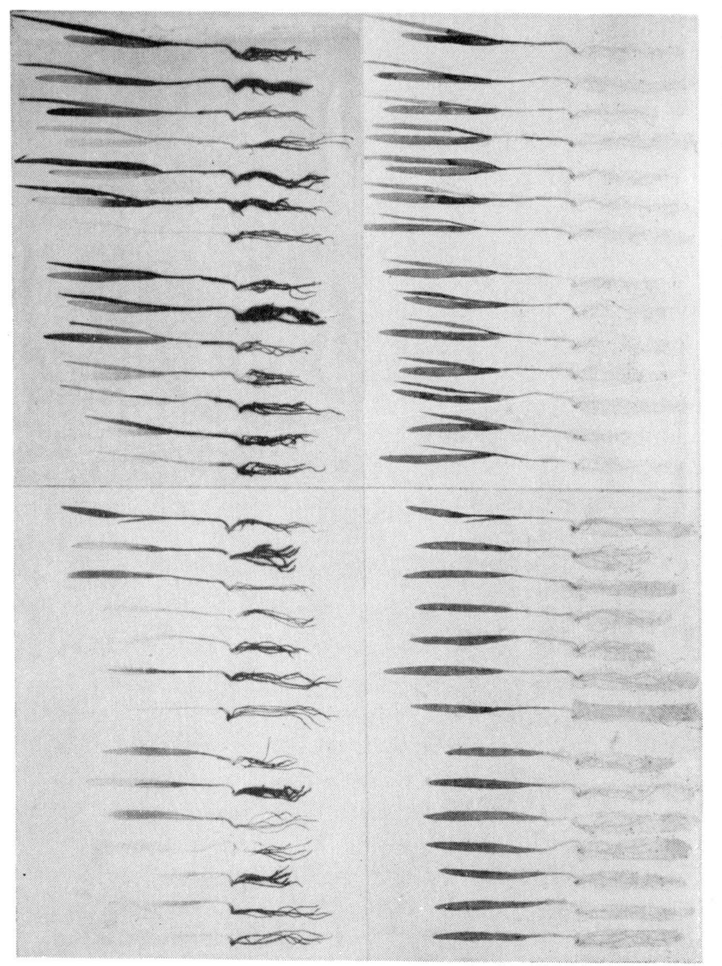

Fig. 8-14. Uptake and distribution of seven C^{14}-labeled tracers from culture solutions by barley seedlings after exposures of 1, 2, 4, and 6 days (left to right). The chemicals (left to right) were 2,4-D, amitrol, MH, urea, monuron, IAA, and dalapon. Culture solution volume, 4 ml; dosage, 0.05 μc.

phosphate produced the strongest autograph of any of the compounds and after 8 days the autograph of the roots was a black blur with all detail obscured. Monuron and simazin moved into the tops by 2 hours and they continued to pile up to the eighth day. Next to move into the tops were, in order of appearance, amitrol and $P^{32}O_4$ by 4 hours; dalapon, IAA, and MH by 8 hours; 2,4-D after 2 days; urea after 4 days, but even after 8 days it was present only in slight traces.

After 8 days concentrations in roots, listed from high to low, were: $P^{32}O_4$, IAA, simazin, monuron, amitrol, 2,4-D, MH, dalapon, and urea. In the tops the order was: simazin, monuron, amitrol, $P^{32}O_4$, dalapon, MH, IAA, 2,4-D, and urea. In 4 and 8 days the concentration of monuron in the first expanded leaf was higher in the top than at the base; simazin was uniform throughout the leaf; $P^{32}O_4$, dalapon, and amitrol were more concentrated in the leaf bases and in leaf number 2. The latter three compounds seem to redistribute in the phloem of stem and leaf; the former two seem to move predominantly in the xylem.

The following 12 C^{14}-labeled compounds plus P^{32} phosphate were tested in cylinders of potato tuber tissue:

2,4-D	sodium phenyl acetate	alanap
2,4,5-T	sodium phosphate	duraset
ATA	monuron	urea
MH	simazin	IAA
sodium benzoate		

Treated cylinders were taken off and freeze dried at 2, 4, 8, and 16 days. As in the previous test (page 133), urea did not penetrate but was largely lost from the tissue cylinder. Of the remaining 12 compounds, monuron and simazin seem not to penetrate living cells and the remaining 10 do move into the living parenchyma. Although monuron seems to move only in cell walls, it penetrated the tissue cylinders to the greatest depth; simazin penetrated at high concentration to a depth of about 5 mm and moved on along the walls to depths of 12, 15, 20, and 23 mm. Table 8-3 presents the data on depth of penetration of the 12 compounds.

From these experiments it seems evident that (1) solutes may accumulate[1] in or on the surface of roots to varying concentrations

[1] The word "accumulate" as used here denotes concentration above that of the ambient solution. No mechanism is implied.

Table 8-3

Penetration of Labeled Compounds into the Tissue of Potato Tuber

	Penetration in millimeters				
Compound	2nd day	4th day	8th day	16th day	Average
Urea	2	1	1	1	1.25
Alanap	2	3	5	5	3.75
Duraset	5	5	5	6	5.25
Simazin[1]	5	6	5	5	5.25
2,4-D	7	7	6	7	6.75
2,4,5-T	7	6	8	8	7.25
Sodium benzoate	8	6	8	7	7.25
IAA[2]	5	6	10	11	8.0
Sodium phenyl acetate	8	10	8	10	9.0
ATA	9	11	15	20	13.5
IAA[3]	10	11	15	20	14.0
PO_4	12	10	20	18	15.0
Simazin[4]	12	15	20	23	17.5
MH	10	15	20	35	20.0
Monuron[5]	23	34	45	55	39.0

[1] Penetration of simazin into parenchyma in high concentration.
[2] Penetration of parenchyma cells.
[3] Penetration of phloem strands.
[4] Penetration of simazin along cell walls.
[5] Penetration of monuron along cell walls.

depending on the particular molecules involved, (2) these solutes may be absorbed into the roots and translocated to the foliage in varying amounts depending upon the molecules involved (2,4-D vs. amitrol) and upon the species (barley vs. cotton), and (3) certain molecules, after an initial period of accumulation by the roots, may move out again into the external solution (2,4-D).

From previous experiments it seems well established that many of these same compounds, when applied to leaves, will migrate from the cuticle to the phloem, move rapidly downward into the roots, and in certain instances leak into the external solution. Finally, it is also evident that certain molecules upon reaching the roots may transfer into the xylem and reenter the foliage (Crafts, 1959). The compounds that seem to be most freely mobile in phloem seem also to transfer to the xylem and reenter the tops in the greatest amounts. Since these can enter from the chlorenchyma into the phloem when they are initially applied to the leaves, it seems evident that they may do likewise when they enter via the transpiration stream, and hence that they may circulate in the plant. Phosphorus undoubtedly does this (Biddulph, 1941; Biddulph *et al.*, 1958); MH apparently circulates freely; dalapon possibly does so (Crafts, 1959; Foy, 1958).

Because radioactive 2,4-D applied to the roots of cotton moves to the tops in greater concentration than it does in barley it appears that the root cells of cotton readily transfer this molecule from cortex to stele whereas those of barley do not.

The same explanation may hold for 2,4-D applied to foliage and moved into the roots via the phloem. Such response may indicate one mechanism of selectivity, because in cotton an appreciable proportion of the translocated 2,4-D might pass back into the xylem whereas in barley the bulk may be lost to the soil. Loss by barley to the external medium may, in a sense, constitute a detoxification mechanism available in 2,4-D-tolerant plants to eliminate the toxic molecules.

Although the cellular concept of plant structure has been of tremendous importance in biology, the concept of the symplast—the continuum of interconnected protoplasts of the plant—and the apoplast—the continuum of nonliving cell-wall material that surrounds and contains the symplast (Münch, 1930)—are also of great usefulness to plant physiologists. The plant body, then, is composed of the apoplast, the symplast, and the intercellular space system.

Radioactive tracers applied to plants are placed on the apoplast. To serve as translocation indicators they must penetrate the apoplast and make contact with the symplast. Applied to foliage, the tracers must move through the cuticle and cell walls, penetrate the ectoplast, and enter the mesoplasm. Here they may migrate with relative freedom to the sieve tubes and translocate to sinks in stem, root tips, and shoot tips. Applied to roots, they have to pass through the cell walls of the epidermis or cortex, penetrate the ectoplast, and enter the mesoplasm where again they may migrate freely across the endodermis and into the stele. Here, because of the high CO_2-low O_2 environment they are lost to the tracheary elements of the xylem (apoplast) where they may translocate rapidly to the foliar regions. And here, some compounds (PO_4, MH, dalapon) may reenter the symplast and so circulate in the plant.

Of the mineral nutrients normally found in plants, sodium,

potassium, phosphorus, sulfur, chlorine, and some nitrogen compounds may retranslocate after their initial movement from roots to leaves; calcium, magnesium, iron, and cobalt are largely fixed in the foliar tissues. These differences are of considerable importance with respect to the nutrition of plants as related to the supplying power of the soil for these various elements.

Recent work with organic compounds excreted by roots (Butler, 1955) has indicated that certain assimilates that are moved into roots from the foliar organs may be released into the soil. This finding is of tremendous significance with respect to soil microbiology, plant competition, and the possible use of chemicals as pesticides for controlling soil-borne organisms.

chapter nine Conclusions

From the large body of literature that has been reviewed, it is apparent that a few salient features stand out and that some problems seem to be nearing a solution.

Uptake of water

The mechanics of the uptake of water by plant roots is less confused than it was four decades ago when several theories were under consideration. Water is apparently absorbed osmotically from the soil by root hairs and cortex cells and it diffuses along the walls and symplast to the endodermis where it must pass the cytoplasm of living cells. Within the stele it is released from the symplast into the cell walls and, seeking the route of least resistance, enters the xylem vessels where it proceeds upward to the stem and leaves. Under conditions of low or zero transpiration this movement seems to take place along a diffusion pressure gradient, the diffusion pressure of water in the symplast and in the stele being lowered by the presence of osmotically active solutes. As transpiration picks up and water loss exceeds water absorption, the pressure lowers until, in the xylem conductors, it may pass the zero atmosphere level and tension sets in. Under these conditions the diffusion pressure of water in the xylem is lowered by the reduced hydrostatic pressure; the gradient from soil to xylem is steepened, and if water is readily available, movement is accelerated.

As soil moisture is lowered, more and more energy is needed to extract water from the soil; in the range of permanent wilting, force to the extent of 16 atmospheres or more may be required to maintain the absorption process. In the wilting state tensile water in the xylem is in a metastable condition, and if disturbed, cavitation may take place and bubbles form and fill many of the vessels or tracheids. However, recent work (Greenidge, Scholander) has proved Dixon's contention that such formation will not completely block flow. Emphasized is the fact that water forms a continuum in the xylem and that, even when the conduits are blocked with air or partly severed by cuts in the stem, it moves around the blocks and continues to supply the demands so long as a fair portion of the xylem remains intact. The controversy over active uptake of water by plant cells (Bennet-Clark, Greenwood, and Barker, 1936; Crafts, Currier, and Stocking, 1949) seems satisfactorily settled (Levitt, 1947, 1948; Ordin, Applewhite, and Bonner, 1956). Few plant physiologists believe that water is actively absorbed in the sense that ions are.

Absorption of ions

The absorption of ions by roots is a more complex process and many theories have been advanced to explain it (Overstreet and Jacobsen, 1952). From the analysis presented on pages 69 to 75, it seems apparent that several rather distinct steps are involved:

(1) Diffusion through the cell walls of root hair or epidermis cells. This in turn may involve free diffusion into the unoriented water of free space and migration along surfaces of cellulose micelles and through the pectin gel.

(2) Adsorption in the cell wall-cytoplasm interface where adsorptive forces of the two cell-wall phases plus those of the lipoprotein mosaic of the ectoplasm are active. Recent work indicates that this process may result in an accumulation of ions to high concentration with a fair portion being reversibly held.

(3) Uptake into the ectoplasm proper. This process is undoubtedly active, requiring the utilization of energy released in metabolism, and it may well involve one or more carrier systems (Lundegardh, 1955). Possibly the endoplasmic reticulum is the structure involved.

(4) Release or migration into the mesoplasm, the continuous phase of the symplast. In this phase reside the mitochondria, the plastids, and some if not all of the microsomes. Endoplasmic reticulum is present in the ectoplast and in the mesoplasm. The nucleus

is imbedded in the mesoplasm, and streaming is characteristic of this phase. The mesoplasm is constantly stirred and the included ions mixed by this streaming, which may well carry ions from one end of a cell to the other and hence accelerate movement to many times the rate brought about by simple diffusion. The mesoplasm is continuous from cell to cell through the cores of the plasmodesmata. Once ions enter the mesoplasm of the root epidermis, their movement across the cortex, endodermis, and ground parenchyma of the stele at a fairly rapid rate is assured. The exact role of the endoplasmic reticulum in this movement is not known at present. This phase of the protoplast may very possibly constitute the system mainly responsible for the absorption and distribution of ions.

(5) Migration into the vacuole. It has become more and more evident in recent years that this step is not essential to transport from soil to xylem. Broyer (1950) has evidence for bypassing of the vacuoles by tagged bromide. Brooks (1938b) showed years ago that the vacuole was the last portion of the cell to be reached by a newly supplied ion. The work of Russell and Shorrocks (1957) and many others indicates that the vacuoles may be the repository for a large quantity of ions; in low-salt plants the vacuoles act as sinks for active uptake whereas in high-salt plants they may be largely bypassed by ions on their way into the xylem. The endoplast (tonoplast), thought by some to be the principal semipermeable barrier of the cell, seems rather to be the guardian of the stored reserves. Movement across it is probably an active process.

So far the process of cellular absorption has been under discussion. Movement of ions from the soil to the xylem conduits is a complex process that is made up of a combination of (1) the processes of free-space movement in the cortex walls plus cellular absorption; (2) migration across the vacuoles of the endodermal cells and hence across the endoplast into the symplast; and finally (3) within the stele, release of ions to the apoplast for movement into the xylem conduits. To speak of free-space movement from soil to xylem is absurd, for it ignores most of what has been learned of the structure and function of roots in the past 100 years.

If the bulk of the cytoplasm of the root cells exists in free space, then the root of the higher plant may be likened to a polythene bag filled with yeast cells. As such it could not transfer solutes from soil to xylem at the rates that have been observed, nor could it possibly develop root pressure to values of 2 or more atmospheres. Nutrition of the meristem would be unexplainable; growth into the soil would be impossible.

If the picture that has been presented is a true one, the generalization that ion absorption is an exchange process would appear to be unnecessary. Although it might apply to excised roots and root segments, in the whole plant salt uptake would be a catenary process with the simultaneous movement of anions, cations, and water. Electrical balance would be maintained and the pH relations that have been observed could be explained on the basis of organic acid synthesis in root cells and CO_2 excretion to the soil.

The overall process of ion uptake into whole plants undoubtedly involves the active participation of the living protoplasm and the expenditure of metabolic energy. The postulation of carrier systems offers an attractive explanation for the mechanics of the process of accumulation, and many such systems have been proposed (see Overstreet and Jacobsen, 1952; Lundegardh, 1955). In the past, however, too many of these have implied a perpetual-motion machine. Attention must now be focused on the way in which energy becomes applied to the process. Although this study requires the use of thermodynamics, the overall process must be more than a thermodynamic concept because a definite machine of known structure is involved, and to ignore structure is to work in a realm of unreality.

Movement of organic materials

As to the processes involved in the movement of organic materials in plants, again a few salient features emerge from the maze of conflicting ideas and controversy of the past decades. The large bulk of evidence points first of all to a mechanism exhibiting a source-sink relation. Many experiments indicate that foods in the plant move from the regions of synthesis to the regions of utilization. This movement implies a polarization not with respect to structure but with respect to function.

Secondly, there is increasing evidence indicating a simultaneous correlated flow of many substances along this common route from source to sink. In other words, transport in the phloem seems dominated by the transport of foods; viruses, labeled indicators, growth regulators, hormones, and assimilates apparently move together.

The foods move along a concentration gradient; the other substances may be carried along only to accumulate in the sinks to concentrations far above those along the channels of movement.

Growing evidence from studies on phloem exudation is to the effect that this process is simply an accelerated form of the natural flow of the assimilate stream. Composition of phloem exudate fits the requirements for the organic nutrition of cells and tissues. Its very existence is a manifestation of the longitudinal permeability of the sieve tubes. Moreover, its seasonal variations in rate and composition fit into the physiology of the plant from which it flows.

One weakness of much past work results from the failure of investigators to realize that the phloem is a distribution system and that its function is not to carry foods only from leaves to roots; its role is to provide organic nutrients for every living nonphotosynthetic cell of the plant. Much of the "leakage," "lateral diffusion," "loss," and so on that has been reported is simply evidence for the normal distributional function of the sieve tubes. If we can grant the symplast concept and the concomitant continuity of the mesoplasm, this distribution may take place from the chloroplast of the mesophyll to the apical cells of the root meristem without the necessity of the molecules passing a single barrier of a semipermeable type. In such a system, the sieve tubes simply represent a highly specialized cell system having unique qualities of permeability and serving as an elongated ramifying structure in which a concentration gradient of foods is transformed to a hydrostatic gradient of solution capable of moving rapidly from source to sink. In view of the specialization of the conduits of the xylem, this phloem system seems to be a reasonable hypothesis. The labeled tracers are of prime importance in overcoming the difficulty of studying this system in its undisturbed state.

To those who have been advocates of the pressure-flow mechanism in the sieve tubes, only one aspect of the concept still lacks satisfactory explanation—namely, the extraordinary permeability of the sieve plates. If the evidence for a semipermeable ectoplast of the functioning sieve tube presented by Schumacher and Currier *et al.* is accepted—and generally it seems to be—then the flow of solution from element to element along the sieve tube must traverse the cores of the protoplasmic strands of the sieve plate. Even taking the area occupied by these strands to be that recently reported by Esau and Cheadle (1959), the linear rate of flow along them must attain values in the hundreds of cm per hour. The classical formulas for calculating resistance to such flow cannot be applied to movement through the intermolecular interstices of cytoplasm, and if they are used in trying to calculate such spaces from known velocities of flow and pressures the values turn out to be improbable (Crafts, 1933).

The writer in 1948 postulated a specialized structure of sieve-tube cytoplasm that involved a skeletonization of the cytoplasmic structure leaving longitudinally arranged polypeptide chains as the principal structural feature. If such could be visualized as making up the mesoplasmic cores of the sieve plate connecting strands, at least part of the resistance would be eliminated.

A recent publication by Mendelssohn (1958) on superfluidity offers an additional possibility. If molecules exist in a highly ordered state, as in liquid helium, they may move in a way that is unaccountable by the classical concepts of physics. In a recent article on bioenergetics Szent-Györgyi (1956) has pointed out that cells may contain little or no random water. Jacobsen (1955) has shown that electropolar groups on surfaces may induce order in adjacent water. Szent-Györgyi suggests that most of the water in the closely packed protoplasm of cells may be in an ordered state. It seems possible that water in this highly ordered state moving between peptide chains ordered in the longitudinal direction may move by a catenary process if sufficient energy were applied at the "upper end." Such a process, devoid of the friction caused by the random motion of thermal agitation, might well provide for the observed rapid flow of phloem exudation. Any process capable of accounting for the latter phenomenon will easily explain normal flow of the assimilate stream through intact phloem.

Spanner (1958) has put forward a new theory that involves a bulk flow of the sieve-tube contents actuated by a mechanism located at the sieve plates. The motive force proposed is electro-osmosis and Spanner claims that the three requirements—namely, a charged membrane, a membrane potential difference, and a porous structure in the membrane—are present in the sieve plate. Spanner attributes maintenance of the potential difference to a cyclic movement of potassium ions into the sieve tube above the sieve plate and thence out of the tube below the plate, the return motion taking place in companion cells or possibly in phloem parenchyma. The starting device for this mechanism would be (1) discharge of sugar into the sieve tubes, (2) uptake of water osmotically leading to a vertical surge in cells neighboring the sieve tube, and (3) flow of potassium ions along the direction of flow in the sieve tubes and counter to this direction in neighboring cells. Once established, this circulation would electrically polarize the sieve plate, causing rapid electro-osmosis through the plate. Thus each sieve plate would contribute its energy to the flowing stream; resistance would be overcome locally rather than being cumulative between source and sink; the circulation of ions causing a maintained polarization of the sieve plates would set up a positive feed back and hence the stable state of the system would be one of motion rather than quiescence.

Spanner's theory is highly speculative and although he claims that experimental evidence supports many of its aspects, he does not present or even cite this evidence. The lack of companion cells in the necessary positions in the phloem of many plants is noted in his paper. Further weaknesses of the theory are the recognized low permeability of the tonoplasts of companion cells and phloem parenchyma, and the lack of an explanation for the ready reversibility of phloem exudation. From earlier work (Crafts, 1936) it is evident that when a stem is cut near the tip, a rapid acropetal flow of sieve-tube sap takes place; when cut near the base, a rapid basipetal motion is found; and, if cut near the center, flow from the top portion is basipetal whereas flow from the basal portion is acropetal. When two cuts are made simultaneously, flow in the portion between the cuts is in the direction of the cuts and hence opposite at the two ends. Furthermore, flow from a given portion of a stem is roughly proportional to the mass of that portion.

Similar tests, using the severed stylets of aphids on willow branches, have been performed by Weatherley *et al.* (1959). These confirm the lack of polarity of sap movement in the sieve tubes and prove the effective length of willow stem segments to lie between 10 cm and 20 cm. The average number of sieve-tube elements in such segments was from 580 to 1160. All of these observations point to the phloem as an inflated elastic system, highly permeable to longitudinal flow in either direction.

Finally, it seems evident that rapid phloem exudation is beyond the realm of speculation; it is a readily demonstrable phenomenon, as can be shown by anyone who will take the trouble to repeat the experiments of Hartig, Nägeli, Moose, Huber, Jahnel, Zimmermann, and many others. If and when we can find a satisfactory explanation for phloem exudation we will need no further theories, for normal phloem transport will be readily explainable on the same basis.

It seems, then, that in the plant are two fundamental conducting systems, both operating by means of demonstrable pressure gradients in elongated systems of permeable conduits. In the xylem, the motion of the stream may be activated by osmotic force developed in rapidly accumulating roots or by transpiration pull resulting from evaporation in the leaves. Resistance to rapid flow in the conducting elements is largely eliminated by loss of the cytoplasm and partial or complete dissolution of the end walls. Structure of the xylem conductors is such that they may operate under either positive pressure or tension. They may be regarded as constituting highly specialized conduits that make up a functional part of the apoplast continuum.

In the phloem, the flow of sap seems to result primarily from the genesis of turgor in the regions of synthesis by osmotic force. Absorption of the total volume of sieve-tube sap in various regions of growth relieves the pressure and activates flow. Return of water to the xylem as visualized by Münch is probably of minor importance, occurring only in regions of starch storage. Resistance to rapid flow in the sieve tubes appears to be lowered by a highly specialized structure of the cytoplasm making up the sieve-plate strands. Structure of the sieve tubes is such that they cannot operate for long under reduced pressure. Rather, when the water balance shifts toward the negative side, the sieve-tube sap may become more concentrated; but so long as the concentration difference between source and sink is maintained by synthesis and utilization, flow must continue, the reduced linear velocity being compensated by increased concentration. Phloem exudation from wilted leaves is mute evidence for maintained turgor in the sieve-tube system.

Thus the sieve-tube system in plants may be considered as constituting a highly specialized system of conduits that serve as a functional part of the symplast continuum. Phloem apparently originated first in plants, for it is present in many of the large algae. The main features of its functional specialization are the continuity of the sieve-element system, the loss of nuclei and endoplasm of sieve elements, and the highly permeable condition of the mesoplasm cores of the sieve-plate connections. Xylem originated only after plants migrated to the land. Specialization of this system went one step further than that of the phloem: the protoplasm was completely removed from its conduits and their cell walls developed internal strengthening to enable them to operate under reduced pressure. Thus were land plants able to provide conducting systems suited to carry on translocation under the variety of conditions imposed upon them by their environments.

Literature Cited

ANDERSSON, F. G., 1929. "Some seasonal changes in the tracheal sap of pear and apricot trees," *Plant Physiol.,* **4:** 459–476.

ARENS, KARL, 1948. "The active membrane. An hypothesis to explain the transfer of water and solutes in plants as depending upon respiration," *Rev. Canad. de Biol.,* **8:** 157–172.

ARISZ, W. H., 1954. "Transport of chloride in the 'symplasm' of *Vallisneria* leaves," *Nature,* **174:** 223–224.

———, 1956. "Significance of the symplasm theory for transport across the root," *Protoplasma,* **46:** 5–62.

ARNON, D. I., 1937. "Ammonium and nitrate nitrogen nutrition of barley at different seasons in relation to hydrogen ion concentration, manganese, copper and oxygen supply," *Soil Sci.,* **44:** 91–121.

ARONOFF, S., 1955. "Translocation from soybean leaves. II," *Plant Physiol.,* **30:** 184–185.

ASKENASY, E., 1896. "Beiträge zur Erklärung des Saftsteigens," *Verh. Naturhist.-med. Ver. Heidelberg,* **5:** 429–448.

BARRIER, G. E., and LOOMIS, W. E., 1957. "Absorption and translocation of 2,4-dichlorophenoxyacetic acid and P^{32} by leaves," *Plant Physiol.,* **32:** 225–231.

BAUER, I., 1906a. "Über die infectiöse Chlorose der Malvaceen," *Sitzungsber. Kgl. Preuss. Akad. Wiss.,* **1:** 11–29.

———, 1906b. "Weitere Mitteilungen über die infektiöse Chlorose der Malvaceen und über einige analoge Erscheinungen bei *Ligustrum* und *Laburnum,*" *Ber. Deutsch. Bot. Ges.,* **24:** 416–428.

BAUER, L., 1949. "Uber den Wanderungsweg fluoreszierenden Farbstoffe in den Siebrohren," *Planta,* **37:** 221–243.

———, 1953. "Zur Frage der Stoffbewegungen in der Pflanze mit-besonderer Berücksichtigung der Wanderung von Fluorochromen," *Planta,* **42:** 367–451.

Beer, M., 1959. "Fine structure of phloem of Cucurbit as revealed by the electron microscope," *Ninth Internatl. Bot. Congr. Proc.,* **2:** 26.

Bennet-Clark, T. A., Greenwood, A. D., and Barker, J. W., 1936. "Water relations and osmotic pressures of plant cells," *New Phytol.,* **35:** 277–291.

Bennett, C. W., 1927. "Virus diseases of raspberries," *Mich. Agr. Expt. Sta. Tech. Bul. 80.*

———, 1934. "Plant tissue relations of sugar-beet curly-top virus," *Jour. Agr. Res.,* **48:** 665–701.

———, 1935. "Studies on properties of the curly-top virus," *Jour. Agr. Res.,* **50:** 211–241.

———, 1937. "Correlation between movement of the curly-top virus and translocation of food in tobacco and sugar beet," *Jour. Agr. Res.,* **54:** 479–502.

———, 1938. "Movement of the virus of sugar beet mosaic," *Phytopath.,* **28:** 668.

———, 1940a. "The relation of viruses to plant tissues," *Bot. Rev.,* **6:** 427–473.

———, 1940b. "Relation of food translocation to the movement of the virus of tobacco mosaic," *Jour. Agr. Res.,* **60:** 361–390.

———, 1943. "Influence of contact period on the passage of viruses from scion to stock in Turkish tobacco," *Phytopath.,* **33:** 818–822.

———, 1944. "Studies on dodder transmission of plant viruses," *Phytopath.,* **34:** 905–932.

———, and Esau, K., 1936. "Further studies on the relation of the curly-top virus to plant tissues," *Jour. Agr. Res.,* **53:** 595–620.

Biddulph, O., 1940. "Absorption and movement of radio phosphorus in bean seedlings," *Plant Physiol.,* **15:** 131–136.

———, 1941. "Diurnal migration of injected radiophosphorus from bean leaves," *Amer. Jour. Bot.,* **28:** 348–352.

———, Biddulph, S., Cory, R., and Koontz, H., 1958. "Circulation patterns for phosphorus, sulfur, and calcium in the bean plant," *Plant Physiol.,* **33:** 293–300.

———, and Cory, R., 1957. "An analysis of translocation in the phloem of the bean plant using THO, P^{32} and $C^{14}O_2$," *Plant Physiol.,* **32:** 608–619.

———, ———, and Biddulph, S., 1956. "The absorption and translocation of sulfur in red kidney bean," *Plant Physiol.,* **31:** 28–33.

———, and Markle, J., 1944. "Translocation of radio phosphorus in the phloem of the cotton plant," *Amer. Jour. Bot.,* **31:** 65–70.

BIDDULPH, S. F., 1956. "Visual indications of S^{35} and P^{32} translocation in the phloem," *Amer. Jour. Bot.,* **43:** 143–148.

BIERBERG, W., 1908. "Die Bedeutung der Protoplasmarotation für den Stoffstransport in den Pflanzen," *Flora,* **99:** 52–80.

BIRCH-HIRSCHFELD, LUISE, 1919. "Untersuchungen über die Ausbreitungsgeschwindigkeit gelöster Stoffe in der Pflanze," *Jahrb. Wiss. Bot.,* **59:** 171–262.

BLACKMAN, G. E., 1955. "Interrelationships between the uptake of 2,4-dichlorophenoxyacetic acid, growth, and ion absorption," in *The Chemistry and Mode of Action of Plant Growth Substances,* Wye College Symposium, edited by Wain and Wightman, London: Butterworths Scientific Publications.

———, 1957. "Selective toxicity in relation to specific differences in retention, penetration, and uptake," *Proc. Intern. Congr. of Crop Protection,* fourth meeting (Hamburg, Germany, September 8–15, 1957, in press).

BODE, H. R., 1923. "Beiträge zur Dynamik der Wasserbewegung in den Gefässpflanzen," *Jahrb. Wiss. Bot.,* **62:** 92–127.

BOEHM, J. A., 1863. "Ueber die Ursache des Saftsteigens in den Pflanzen," *Sitzungsber. Akad. Wiss. in Wien.,* **48:** 10–24.

BÖHNING, R. H., KENDALL, W. A., and LINCK, A. J., 1953. "Effect of temperature and sucrose on growth and translocation in tomato," *Amer. Jour. Bot.,* **40:** 150–153.

———, SWANSON, C. A., and LINCK, A. J., 1952. "The effect of hypocotyl temperature on translocation of carbohydrates from bean leaves," *Plant Physiol.,* **27:** 417–421.

BOSE, J. C., 1923. *The physiology of the ascent of sap,* New York, London: Longmans, Green and Co.

BOUCHERIE, A., 1840. "Mémoire sur la Conservation des bois," *Compt. rend.,* **10:** 685–689.

BRIGGS, G. E., and ROBERTSON, R. N., 1957. "Apparent free space," *Ann. Rev. Plant Physiol.,* **8:** 11–30.

BROOKS, S. C., 1938a. "The chemical nature of the plasma membrane as revealed by permeability," *Amer. Naturalist,* **72:** 124–140.

———, 1938b. "Penetration of radioactive ions, their accumulation by protoplasm of living cells (*Nitella coronata*)," *Soc. Exptl. Biol. and Medicine Proc.,* **38:** 856–858.

———, 1943a. "Intake and loss of ions by living cells. I. Eggs and larvae of *Arabacia punctulata* and *Asterias forbesi* exposed to phosphate and sodium ions," *Biol. Bul.,* **84:** 213–225.

———, 1943b. "Intake and loss by living cells. II. Early changes of phosphate content of *Fundulus* eggs," *Biol. Bul.,* **84:** 226–239.

BROYER, T. C., 1950. "Further observations on the absorption and translocation of inorganic solutes using radioactive isotopes with plants," *Plant Physiol.*, **25:** 367–376.

Broyer, T. C., 1956. "Current views on solute movement into plant roots," *Amer. Soc. Hort. Sci. Proc.*, **67:** 570–586.

Bukovac, M. J., and Wittwer, S. H., 1957. "Absorption and mobility of foliar applied nutrients," *Plant Physiol.*, **32:** 428–435.

———, ———, and Tukey, H. B., 1956. "Anesthetization by di-ethyl ether and the transport of foliar applied radio calcium," *Plant Physiol.*, **31:** 254–255.

Butler, G. W., 1953a. "Ion uptake by young wheat plants," *Physiol. Plantarum*, **6:** 594–671.

———, 1953b. "Ion uptake by young wheat plants. II. The apparent free space of wheat roots," *Physiol. Plantarum*, **6:** 662–671.

———, 1955. "Minerals and living cells," *Jour. N. Z. Inst. Chem.*, **19:** 66–75.

Candolle, A. P. de, 1832. *Physiologie vegetale,* Vol. I, Paris: Bechet Jeune.

Cannon, W. A., 1932. "Absorption of oxygen by roots when the shoot is in darkness or in light," *Plant Physiol.*, **7:** 673–684.

Canny, M. J., 1959. "Note on the measurement of translocation of photosynthate in very short times," *Can. Jour. Biochem. Physiol.*, **37:** 1390–1392.

Cheadle, V., and Whitford, N. B., 1941. "Observations on the phloem in the Monocotyledoneae. I. The occurrence and phytogenetic specialization in structure of the sieve tubes in the metaphloem," *Amer. Jour. Bot.*, **28:** 623–627.

Clements, H. F., 1940. "Movement of organic solutes in the sausage tree, *Kigelia africana*," *Plant Physiol.*, **15:** 689–700.

Clor, M. A., 1951. "Studies on translocation of 2,4-D in cotton plants," Master's thesis, University of California, Davis.

Colwell, R. N., 1942a. "Translocation in plants with special reference to the mechanism of phloem transport as indicated by studies on phloem exudation and on the movement of radioactive phosphorus," Ph.D. thesis, University of California.

———, 1942b. "The use of radioactive phosphorus in translocation studies," *Amer. Jour. Bot.*, **29:** 798–807.

Cooil, B. J., 1941. "Significance of phloem exudate of *Cucurbita pepo* with reference to translocation of organic materials," *Plant Physiol.*, **16:** 61–84.

Cooke, A. R., 1956. "A possible mechanism of action of the urea type herbicides," *Weeds,* **4:** 397–398.

Copeland, E. B., 1902. "The rise of the transpiration stream: an historical and critical discussion," *Bot. Gaz.*, **34:** 161–193, 260–283.

CRAFTS, A. S., 1931. "Movement of organic materials in plants," *Plant Physiol.*, **6:** 1–41.

———, 1932. "Phloem anatomy, exudation, and transport of organic nutrients in cucurbits," *Plant Physiol.*, **7:** 183–225.

———, 1933. "Sieve-tube structure and translocation in the potato," *Plant Physiol.*, **8:** 81–104.

———, 1936. "Further studies on exudation in cucurbits," *Plant Physiol.*, **11:** 63–79.

———, 1938. "Translocation in plants," *Plant Physiol.*, **13:** 791–814.

———, 1939a. "The relation between structure and function of the phloem," *Amer. Jour. Bot.*, **26:** 172–177.

———, 1939b. "Movement of viruses, auxins, and chemical indicators in plants," *Bot. Rev.*, **5:** 471–504.

———, 1939c. "The protoplasmic properties of sieve tubes," *Protoplasma*, **33:** 389–398.

———, 1939d. "Solute transport in plants," *Science*, **90:** 337–338.

———, 1948. "Movement of materials in phloem as influenced by the porous nature of the tissues," in *Interaction of water and porous materials*, Faraday Soc. Disc. No. 3, 153–159.

———, 1951. "Movement of assimilates, viruses, growth regulators, and chemical indicators in plants," *Bot. Rev.*, **17:** 203–284.

———, 1954. "Composition of the sap of xylem and phloem and its relation to the nutrition of the plant," *Colloque analyse des plantes et problèmes des engrais minéraux*, pp. 18–21. Int. Cong. Botany, 8th, Paris, 1954.

———, 1956a. "Translocation of herbicides. I. The mechanism of translocation: Methods of study with C^{14}-labeled 2,4-D," *Hilgardia*, **26:** 287–334.

———, 1956b. "Translocation of herbicides. II. Absorption and translocation of 2,4-D by wild morning glory," *Hilgardia*, **26:** 335–365.

———, 1958. "Studies on translocated herbicides," *Span*, No. 3 (October, 1958), pp. 5–11. Shell Public Health and Agricultural News. St. Helen's Court, Great St. Helen's, London E.C. 3.

———, 1959. "Further studies on the comparative mobility of labeled herbicides," *Plant Physiol.*, **34:** 613–620.

———, and BROYER, T. C., 1938. "Migration of salts and water into xylem of the roots of higher plants," *Amer. Jour. Bot.*, **25:** 529–535.

———, CURRIER, H. B., and STOCKING, C. R., 1949. *Water in the physiology of plants*, Waltham, Mass.: Chronica Botanica Co.

Crafts, A. S., and Foy, C. L., 1959. "Autoradiography of radioactive dalapon," *Down-to-Earth*, **14:** 2–6.

———, and Lorenz, O., 1944a. "Fruit growth and food transport in cucurbits," *Plant Physiol.*, **19:** 131–138.

———, ———, 1944b. "Composition of fruits and phloem exudate of cucurbits," *Plant Physiol.*, **19:** 326–337.

———, and Yamaguchi, S., 1958. "Comparative tests on the uptake and distribution of labeled herbicides by *Zebrina pendula* and *Tradescantia fluminensis*," *Hilgardia*, **27:** 421–454.

———, ———, 1960. "Absorption of herbicides by roots," *Amer. Jour. Bot.*, **47:** 248–255.

Crowdy, S. H., 1958. "Uptake and translocation of organic chemicals by plants," Imperial Chem. Indus. Ltd., Jealotts Hill Res. Sta. Mimeo. 16 pages.

———, Green, A. P., Grove, J. F., McCloskey, P., and Morrison, A., 1959a. "The translocation of antibiotics in plants 3. The estimation of griseofulvin relatives in plant tissue," *Biochem. Jour.*, **72:** 230–241.

———, Grove, J. F., and McCloskey, P., 1959b. "The translocation of antibiotics in plants 4. Systemic fungicidal activity and chemical structure in griseofulvin relatives," *Biochem. Jour.*, **72:** 241–249.

———, and Pramer, D., 1955. "Movement of antibiotics in higher plants," *Chemistry and Industry*, 1955, pp. 160–162.

Currier, H. B., Esau, K., and Cheadle, V. I., 1955. "Plasmolytic studies of phloem," *Amer. Jour. Bot.*, **42:** 68–81.

Curtis, Otis F., 1920a. "The upward translocation of foods in woody plants. I. Tissues concerned in translocation," *Amer. Jour. Bot.*, **7:** 101–124.

———, 1920b. "The upward translocation of foods in woody plants. II. Is there normally an upward transfer of storage foods from the roots or trunk to the growing points?" *Amer. Jour. Bot.*, **7:** 286–295.

———, 1925. "Studies on the tissues concerned in the transfer of solutes in plants. The effect on the upward transfer of solutes of cutting the xylem as compared with that of cutting the phloem," *Ann. Bot.*, **39:** 573–585.

———, 1929. "Studies on the solute translocation in plants. Experiments indicating that translocation is dependent on the activity of living cells," *Amer. Jour. Bot.*, **16:** 154–168.

———, 1935. *The translocation of solutes in plants*, New York: McGraw-Hill Book Co.

———, and Asai, G. N., 1939. "Evidence relative to the supposed permeability of sieve-tube protoplasm," *Amer. Jour. Bot.*, **26:** 165–175.

CZAPEK, FRIEDRICH, 1897. "Ueber die Leitungswege der organischen Baustoffe im Pflanzenkorper," *Sitzungsber. der Kaiserlichen Akad. der Wiss.*, **66:** 117–170.

DAVIS, E. F., 1929. "Some chemical and physiological studies on the nature and transmission of infectious chlorosis in variegated plants," *Ann. Mo. Bot. Garden*, **16:** 145–226.

DAVIS, G. E., and SMITH, ORA, 1950. "Physiological studies on the toxicity of 2,4-D," *N. E. Weed Control Conf. 4th Ann. Proc.*, 92–101.

DAY, B. E., 1952. "The absorption and translocation of 2,4-dichlorophenoxyacetic acid by bean plants," *Plant Physiol.*, **27:** 143–152.

DELEANO, NICOLAS T., 1911. "Ueber die Ableitung der Assimilate durch die intakten, die chloroformierten und die plasmolysierten Blattstiele der Laubblatter," *Jahrb. Wiss. Bot.*, **49:** 129–186.

DE VRIES, H., 1885. "Ueber die Bedeutung der Circulation und der Rotation des Protoplasma für das Stofftransport in der Pflanze," *Bot. Zeit.*, **43:** 1–6; 16–26.

DIMOND, A. E., and HORSFALL, J. G., 1959. "Plant chemotherapy," *Ann. Rev. Plant Physiol.*, **10:** 257–276.

DIXON, H. H., 1914. *Transpiration and the ascent of sap in plants*, London: Macmillan and Co., 216 pages.

———, 1923. "Transport of organic substances in plants," Notes from the Botanical School of Trinity College, Dublin, **3:** 207–215.

———, and BALL, NIGEL G., 1922. "Transport of organic substances in plants," *Nature*, **109:** 236–237.

———, ———, 1923. "On the channels of transport from the storage organs of the seedlings of *Lodoicea Phoenix* and *Vicia*," Notes from the Botanical School of Trinity College, Dublin, **3:** 235–245.

———, and JOLY, J., 1894. "On the ascent of sap," *Roy. Soc. London Proc.*, **57B:** 3.

DUGGER, W. M., JR., HUMPHREYS, T. E., and CALHOUN, B., 1957. "The influence of boron on starch phosphorylase and its significance in translocation of sugars in plants," *Plant Physiol.*, **32:** 364–370.

DUTROCHET, H., 1827. "Nouvelles observations sur l'endosmose et l'exosmose, et sur la cause de ce double phénomène," *Annal. de Chimie*, **35:** 393–400.

Elfring, F., 1882. "Ueber die Wasserleitung im Holz," *Bot. Ztg. S 707,* **40:** Col. 707–723.

Engard, C. J., 1939a. "Translocation of carbohydrates in the Cuthbert raspberry," *Bot. Gaz.,* **100:** 439–464.

——, 1939b. "Translocation of nitrogenous substances in the Cuthbert raspberry," *Bot. Gaz.,* **101:** 1–34.

——, 1944. "Organogenesis in *Rubus,*" *Univ. Hawaii Res. Publ. 21,* 234 pages.

Eppley, R. W., and Blinks, L. R., 1957. "Cell space and apparent free space in the red alga *Porphyra perforata,*" *Plant Physiol.,* **32:** 63–64.

Epstein, E., 1955. "Passive permeation and active transport of ions in plant roots," *Plant Physiol.,* **30:** 529–535.

——, 1956. "Mineral nutrition of plants: mechanisms of uptake and transport," *Ann. Rev. Plant Physiol.,* **7:** 1–24.

——, 1960. "Spaces, barriers, and ion carriers: ion absorption by plants," *Amer. Jour. Bot.,* **47:** 393–399.

Errera, L., 1886. "Une expérience sur l'ascension de la sève chez les plantes," *Compt. rend. de la Soc. Roy. de Belgique Bull.,* **25:** (C.R.) 24–32.

Esau, K., 1938. "Some anatomical aspects of plant virus disease problems," *Bot. Rev.,* **4:** 548–579.

——, 1939. "Development and structure of the phloem tissue," *Bot. Rev.,* **5:** 373–432.

——, 1941. "Phloem anatomy of tobacco affected with curly top and mosaic," *Hilgardia,* **13:** 437–490.

——, 1943. "Origin and development of primary vascular tissues in seed plants," *Bot. Rev.,* **9:** 125–206.

——, 1947. "A study of some sieve-tube inclusions," *Amer. Jour. Bot.,* **34:** 224–233.

——, 1948. "Phloem structure in the grape vine and its seasonal changes," *Hilgardia,* **18:** 217–296.

——, 1950. "Development and structure of the phloem tissue. II," *Bot. Rev.,* **16:** 67–114.

——, 1953. *Plant anatomy,* New York: John Wiley and Sons, 735 pages.

——, and Cheadle, V. I., 1959. "Size of pores and their contents in sieve elements of dicotyledons," *Nat. Acad. Sci. Proc.,* **45:** 156–162.

——, ——, and Gifford, E. M., 1953. "Comparative structure and possible trends of specialization of the phloem," *Amer. Jour. Bot.,* **40:** 9–19.

——, Currier, H. B., and Cheadle, V. I., 1957. "Physiology of phloem," *Ann. Rev. Plant Physiol.,* **8:** 349–374.

ESCHRICH, W., 1953. "Beiträge zur Kenntnis der Wundsiebröhren-Entwicklung bei *Impatiens Holsti*," *Planta*, **43:** 37–74.
EWART, A. J., 1903. *On the physics and physiology of protoplasmic streaming in plants*, Oxford, England.

FANG, S. C., and BUTTS, J. S., 1954a. "Studies on plant metabolism. III. Absorption, translocation and metabolism of radioactive 2,4-D in corn and wheat seedlings," *Plant Physiol.*, **29:** 56–60.
———, ———, 1954b. "Studies in plant metabolism. IV. Comparative effects of 2,4-dichlorophenoxyacetic acid and other plant growth regulators on phosphorus metabolism in bean plants," *Plant Physiol.*, **29:** 365–368.
———, JAWORSKI, E. G., LOGAN, A. V., FREED, V. H., and BUTTS, J. S., 1951. "The absorption of radioactive 2,4-dichlorophenoxyacetic acid and the translocation of C^{14} by bean plants," *Arch. Biochem. and Biophys.*, **32:** 249–255.
FISCHER, ALFRED, 1883. "Das Siebrohrensystem von *Cucurbita*," *Ber. Deutsch Bot. Ges.*, **1:** 276–279.
———, 1884. *Untersuchungen über das Siebröhren-System der Cucurbitaceen*, Berlin: Gebrüder Borntraeger.
———, 1885. "Ueber den Inhalt der Siebrohren in der unverletzter Pflanze," *Ber. Deutsch. Bot. Ges.*, **3:** 230–239.
FOY, C. L., 1958. "Studies on the absorption, distribution and metabolism of 2,2-dichloropropionic acid in relation to phytotoxicity." Ph.D. dissertation, University of California, Davis.
FREELAND, R. O., 1936. "Effect of transpiration upon the absorption and distribution of mineral salts in plants," *Amer. Jour. Bot.*, **23:** 355–362.

GALLUP, A. H., and GUSTAFSON, F. G., 1952. "Absorption and translocation of radioactive 2,4-dichloro-5-iodo^{131} phenoxyacetic acid by green plants," *Plant Physiol.*, **27:** 603–612.
GAUCH, H. G., and DUGGER, W. M., JR., 1953. "The role of boron in the translocation of sucrose," *Plant Physiol.*, **28:** 457–466.
GODLEWSKI, E., 1884. "Zur Theorie der Wasserbewegung in den Pflanzen," *Jahrb. Wiss. Bot.*, **15:** 569–630.
GREENIDGE, K. N. H., 1954. "Studies in the physiology of forest trees. I. Physical factors affecting the movement of moisture," *Amer. Jour. Bot.*, **41:** 807–811.
———, 1955a. "Studies in the physiology of forest trees. II. Experimental studies of fracture of stretched water columns in transpiring trees," *Amer. Jour. Bot.*, **42:** 28–37.
———, 1955b. "Studies in the physiology of forest trees. III. The

effect of drastic interruption of conducting tissues on moisture movement," *Amer. Jour. Bot.*, **42:** 582–587.

HABERLANDT, G., 1914. *Physiological plant anatomy,* Translation from the fourth German edition by M. Drummond, pp. 327–336, London: Macmillan and Co.

HALES, STEPHEN, 1769. *Vegetable staticks,* 1726–7. Vol. I, Edition 3, London.

HANSON, J. B., and BIDDULPH, O., 1953. "The diurnal variation in the translocation of minerals across bean roots," *Plant Physiol.,* **28:** 356–370.

HANSTEIN, JOHANNES, 1860. "Ueber die Leitung des Saftes durch die Rinde," *Jahrb. Wiss. Bot.,* **2:** 392–446.

HARTIG, R., 1882. "Ueber die Ursache der Wasserbewegung in transpirirenden Pflanzen," *Flora,* **66** (1883): 11–16.

HARTIG, TH., 1837. "Vergleichende Untersuchungen über die Organisation des Stammes der ein heimischen Waldbäume," *Jahresber. Forsch. Forstwissensch. und Forstl. Naturkunde,* **1:** 125–168.

———, 1854. "Ueber die Quersheidewande zwischen den einselnen Gliedern der Siebrohren in *Cucurbita pepo,*" *Bot. Zeit.,* **12:** 51–54.

———, 1858a. "Ueber die Bewegung des Saftes in den Holzpflanzen," *Bot. Zeit.,* **16:** 329–335; 337–342.

———, 1858b. "Ueber den Herbstsaft der Holzpflanzen," *Bot. Zeit.,* **16:** 369–370.

HAUN, J. R., and PETERSON, J. H., 1954. "Translocation of 3-(*p*-chlorophenyl)-1,1-dimethylurea in plants," *Weeds,* **3:** 177–187.

HAY, J. R., and THIMANN, K. V., 1956. "The fate of 2,4-dichlorophenoxyacetic acid in bean seedlings. II. Translocation," *Plant Physiol.,* **31:** 446–451.

HEINE, H., 1885. "Ueber die physiologische Function der Starkescheide," *Ber. Deutsch. Bot. Ges.,* **3:** 189–194.

HEPTON, C. E. L., PRESTON, R. D., and RIPLEY, G. W., 1955. "Electron microscopic observations on the structure of the sieve plates in Cucurbita," *Nature,* **176:** 868–870.

HEWITT, S. P., and CURTIS, O. F., 1948. "The effect of temperature on loss of dry matter and carbohydrate from leaves by respiration and translocation," *Amer. Jour. Bot.,* **35:** 746–755.

HILDEBRAND, E. M., 1942. "Rapid transmission techniques for stone-fruit viruses," *Science,* **95:** 52.

———, and CURTIS, O. F., 1942. "A darkening technique for inducing virus symptoms in mature as well as in growing leaves," *Science,* **95:** 390.

HILL, A. W., 1901. "The histology of sieve-tube of Pinus," *Ann. Bot.,* **15:** 575–611.

———, 1908. "The histology of the sieve-tubes of Angiosperms," *Ann. Bot.,* **22:** 245–290.

HOAGLAND, D. R., 1936. *The plant as a metabolic unit in the soil-plant system,* University of California Press.

———, 1937. "Some aspects of the salt nutrition of higher plants," *Bot. Rev.,* **3:** 307–334.

———, 1944. *Lectures on the inorganic nutrition of plants,* Waltham, Mass.: Chronica Botanica Co.

———, and BROYER, T. C., 1936. "General nature of the process of salt accumulation by roots with description of experimental methods," *Plant Physiol.,* **11:** 471–507.

———, and DAVIS, A. R., 1923. "The composition of the cell sap of the plant in relation to the absorption of ions," *Jour. Gen. Physiol.,* **5:** 629–646.

———, and STEWARD, F. C., 1939. "Metabolism and salt absorption by plants," *Nature,* **143:** 1031.

HOPE, A. B., 1953. "Salt uptake by root tissue cytoplasm: the relation between uptake and external concentration," *Austral. Jour. Biol. Sci.,* **6:** 396–409.

———, and ROBERTSON, R. N., 1953. "Bioelectric experiments and the properties of plant protoplasm," *Austral. Jour. Sci.,* **15:** 197–203.

———, and STEVENS, P. G., 1952. "Electric potential differences in bean roots and their relation to salt uptake," *Austral. Jour. Sci. Res.* B, **5:** 335–343.

HORWITZ, L., 1958. "Some simplified mathematical treatments of translocation in plants," *Plant Physiol.,* **33:** 81–93.

HOUSTON, B. R., ESAU, K., and HEWITT, W. B., 1947. "The mode of vector feeding and the tissues involved in the transmission of Pierce's disease virus in grape and alfalfa," *Phytopath.,* **37:** 247–253.

HUBER, B., 1937. "Methoden, Ergebnisse und Probleme der neuen Baumphysiologie," *Ber. Deutsch Bot. Ges.,* **55:** 46–62.

———, 1939. "Das Siebrohrensystem unserer Baume und seine jahreszeitlichen Veranderungen," *Jahrb. Wiss. Bot.,* **88:** 176–242.

———, 1941. "Gesichertes und Problematisches in der Wanderung der Assimilate," *Ber. Deutsch Bot. Ges.,* **59:** 181–194.

———, 1942. "Die Siebrohren der Pflanzen als Nahrungsquelle fremder Organismen und als Transportbahnen von Krankheits-Keimen," *Biol. Gen.,* **16:** 310–343.

Huber, B., 1953. "Die Gewinnung des Eschenmanna—eine Nutzung von Siebrohrensaft," *Ber. Deutsch Bot. Ges.,* **66:** 341–346.

———, and Rouschal, Ernst, 1938. "Anatomische und zellphysiologische Beobachtungen am Siebrohrensystem der Baume," *Ber. Deutsch Bot. Ges.,* **56:** 380–391.

———, Schmidt, E., and Jahnel, H., 1937. "Untersuchungen über den Assimilatstrom. I," *Tharandter Forstl. Jahrb.,* **88:** 1017–1050.

Hull, H. M., 1952. "Carbohydrate translocation in tomato and sugar beet with particular reference to temperature effect," *Amer. Jour. Bot.,* **39:** 661–669.

Hylmö, B., 1953. "Transpiration and ion absorption," *Physiol. Plantarum,* **6:** 333–405.

———, 1955. "Passive components in the ion absorption," *Physiol. Plantarum,* **8:** 433–449.

Jacobson, B., 1955. "On the interpretation of dielectric constants of aqueous macromolecular solutions. Hydration of macromolecules," *Jour. Amer. Chem. Soc.,* **77:** 2919–2926.

Jacobson, L., 1955. "Carbon dioxide fixation and ion absorption in barley roots," *Plant Physiol.,* **30:** 264–269.

———, and Overstreet, R., 1947. "A study of the mechanism of ion absorption by plant roots using radioactive elements," *Amer. Jour. Bot.,* **34:** 415–420.

———, ———, Carlson, R. M., and Chastain, J. A., 1957. "The effect of pH and temperature on the absorption of potassium and bromide by barley roots," *Plant Physiol.,* **32:** 658–662.

———, ———, King, H. M., and Handley, R., 1950. "A study of potassium absorption by barley roots," *Plant Physiol.,* **25:** 639–647.

Janse, J. M., 1887. "Die Mitwirkung der Markstrahlen bei Wasserbewegung im Holz," *Jahr. Wiss. Bot.,* **18:** 1–69.

———, 1913. "Der Aufsteigende Strom in der Pflanze. II," *Jahrb. Wiss. Bot.,* **52:** 509–602.

Jenny, H., 1951. "Contact phenomena between adsorbents and their significance in plant nutrition," in *Mineral nutrition of plants,* Madison, Wis.: University of Wisconsin Press.

———, and Overstreet, R., 1939. "Cation interchange between plant roots and soil colloids," *Soil Sci.,* **47:** 257–272.

Kastens, Emma, 1924. "Beitrage zur Kenntnis der Funktion die Siebrohren," *Mitteilungen aus dem Institut fur allgemeine Botanik in Hamburg,* **6:** 33–70.

KELLER, W., 1956. *The Bible as history.* New York: William Morrow and Co.

KENDALL, W. A., 1952. "The effect of intermittently varied petiole temperature on carbohydrate translocation from bean leaves," *Plant Physiol.,* **27:** 631–633.

———, 1955. "Effect of certain metabolic inhibitors on translocation of P^{32} in bean plants," *Plant Physiol.,* **30:** 347–350.

KENNEDY, J. S., and MITTLER, T. E., 1953. "A method for obtaining phloem sap via the mouth parts of aphids," *Nature,* **171:** 528.

KESSLER, B., and MOSCICKI, Z. W., 1958. "Effect of triiodobenzoic acid and maleic hydrazide upon the transport of foliar applied calcium and iron," *Plant Physiol.,* **33:** 70–72.

KIDD, F., 1918. "Translocation in plant tissues," *New Phytol.,* **17:** 44–45.

KNIGHT, T. A., 1801. "Account of some experiments on the ascent of sap in trees," *Phil. Trans. Roy. Soc. London.*

KOONTZ, H., and BIDDULPH, O., 1957. "Factors affecting absorption and translocation of foliar applied phosphorus," *Plant Physiol.,* **32:** 463–470.

KRAMER, P. J., 1957. "Outer space in plants," *Science,* **125:** 633–635.

KRAUS, GREGOR, 1885. "Ueber die Susammensetzung des Siebrohrensaftes der Kurbise und alkalisch reagirende Zellsafte," *Abh. Natur. Ges. Halle,* **16:** 376–387.

KURSANOV, A. L., 1956a. "Analysis of the movement of substances in plants by means of radioactive isotopes," in *Peaceful Uses of Atomic Energy,* Internatl. Conf. on the Peaceful Uses of Atomic Energy, Proc., **12:** 165–169.

———, 1956b. "Recent advances in plant physiology in the U.S.S.R.," *Ann. Rev. Plant Physiol.,* **7:** 401–436.

KYLIN, A., and HYLMÖ, B., 1957. "Uptake and transport of sulphate in wheat. Active and passive components," *Physiol. Plantarum,* **10:** 467–484.

LACKEY, C. F., 1948. "Attraction of vascular bundles for dodder haustoria in healthy and curly-top infected beet petioles," *Phytopath.,* **38:** 916.

LAINE, T., 1934. "On the absorption of electrolytes by the cut roots of plants and the chemistry of plant exudation sap," *Acta Bot. Fenn.,* **16:** 1–64.

LECOMTE, H., 1889. "Contribution à l'étude du liber des Angiospermes," *Ann. Sci. Nat. Bot.,* Series 7, **10:** 193–324.

LEONARD, O. A., 1936. "Seasonal study of tissue function and organic solute movement in the sunflower," *Plant Physiol.,* **11:** 25–61.

LEONARD, O. A., 1938. "Transformation of sugars in sugar beet and corn leaves and invertase activity," *Amer. Jour. Bot.,* **25:** 78–83.

———, 1939. "Translocation of carbohydrates in the sugar beet," *Plant Physiol.,* **14:** 55–74.

———, and CRAFTS, A. S., 1956. "Translocation of herbicides. III. Uptake and distribution of radioactive 2,4-D by brush species," *Hilgardia,* **26:** 366–415.

LEONHARDT, H., 1940. "Beiträge zur Kenntnis der Lachniden, der wichtigsten Tannenhonigtauerzeuger," *Z. angew Entomol.,* **27:** 208–272.

LEVITT, J., 1947. "The thermodynamics of active (non-osmotic) water absorption," *Plant Physiol.,* **22:** 514–525.

———, 1948. "The role of active water absorption in auxin-induced water uptake by aerated potato discs," *Plant Physiol.,* **23:** 505–515.

———, 1957. "The significance of Apparent Free Space (AFS) in ion absorption," *Physiol. Plantarum,* **10:** 882–888.

LINDER, P. J., BROWN, J. W., and MITCHELL, J. W., 1949. "Movement of externally applied phenoxy compounds in bean plants in relation to conditions favoring carbohydrate translocation," *Bot. Gaz.,* **110:** 628–632.

———, CRAIG, J. C., JR., and WALTON, T. R., 1957. "Movement of C^{14} tagged alpha-methoxyphenylacetic acid out of roots," *Plant Physiol.,* **32:** 572–575.

———, ———, COOPER, F. E., and MITCHELL, J. W., 1958. "Movement of 2,3,6-trichlorobenzoic acid from one plant to another through their root systems," *Agric. and Food Chem.,* **6:** 356–357.

LOOMIS, W. E., 1945. "Translocation of carbohydrates in maize," *Science,* **101:** 398–400.

LUNDEGARDH, H., 1950. "The translocation of salts and water through wheat roots," *Physiol. Plantarum,* **3:** 103–151.

———, 1955. "Mechanisms of absorption, transport, accumulation, and secretion of ions," *Ann. Rev. Plant Physiol.,* **6:** 1–24.

MALPIGHI, MARCELLUS, 1675 and 1679. *Die anatomie der pflanzen,* Leipzig: Wilhelm Engelmann.

MANGHAM, S., 1917. "On the mechanism of translocation in plant tissues. An hypothesis, with special reference to sugar conduction in sieve-tubes," *Ann. Bot.,* **31:** 293–311.

MARTENS, P., and PIGNEUR, H., 1947. "Les espaces intercellulaires du tissue criblé," *Cellule,* **51:** 185–192.

MASKELL, E. J., and MASON, T. G., 1929a. "Studies on the transport of nitrogenous substances in the cotton plant. I. Preliminary observations on the downward transport of nitrogen in the stem," *Ann. Bot.,* **43:** 205–231.

MASKELL, E. J., and MASON, T. G., 1929b. "Studies on the transport of nitrogenous substances in the cotton plant. II. Observations on concentration gradients," *Ann. Bot.,* **43:** 615–652.

———, ———, 1930a. "Studies on the transport of nitrogenous substances in the cotton plant. III. The relation between longitudinal movement and concentration gradients in the bark," *Ann. Bot.,* **44:** 1–29.

———, ———, 1930b. "The interpretation of the effects of ringing, with special reference to the lability of the nitrogen compounds of the bark," *Ann. Bot.,* **44:** 234–267.

———, ———, 1930c. "Movement to the boll," *Ann. Bot.,* **44:** 657–688.

MASON, T. G., 1923. "A note on the growth and transport of organic substances in Bitter Cassava," Notes from the Botanical School of Trinity College, Dublin, **3:** 216–221.

———, and LEWIN, C. J., 1926. "On the rate of carbohydrate transport in the Greater Yam, *Discorea alata," Linn. Sci. Proc. Roy. Dublin Soc.,* **18:** 203–205.

———, and MASKELL, E. J., 1928a. "Studies on the transport of carbohydrates in the cotton plant. I. A study of diurnal variation in the carbohydrates of leaf, bark and wood and of the effects of ringing," *Ann. Bot.,* **42:** 1–65.

———, ———, 1928b. "Studies on the transport of carbohydrates in the cotton plant. II. The factors determining the rate and the direction of movement of sugars," *Ann. Bot.,* **42:** 571–636.

———, ———, 1931. "Further studies on transport in the cotton plant. I. Preliminary observations on the transport of phosphorus, potassium and calcium," *Ann. Bot.,* **45:** 125–173.

———, and PHILLIS, E., 1937. "The migration of solutes," *Bot. Rev.,* **3:** 47–71.

MENDELSSOHN, K., 1958. "Superfluids," *Science,* **127:** 215–221.

MINSHALL, W. H., 1954. "Translocation path and place of action of 3-(4-chlorophenyl)-1,1-dimethylurea in bean and tomato," *Canad. Jour. Bot.,* **32:** 795–798.

MITCHELL, J. W., and BROWN, J. W., 1946. "Movement of 2,4-dichlorophenoxyacetic acid stimulus and its relation to the translocation of organic food materials in plants," *Bot. Gaz.,* **107:** 393–407.

———, DUGGER, W. M., JR., and GAUCH, H. G., 1953. "Increased translocation of plant-growth modifying substances due to application of boron," *Science,* **118:** 354–355.

MITTLER, T. E., 1953. "Amino-acids in phloem sap and their excretion by aphids," *Nature,* **172:** 207.

———, 1957a. "Studies on the feeding and nutrition of *Tuberolachnus salignus.* I. The uptake of phloem sap," *Jour. Exptl. Biol.,* **34:** 334–341.

———, 1957b. "Studies on the feeding and nutrition of *Tuberolachnus salignus.* II. The nitrogen and sugar composition of ingested phloem sap and excreted honey dew," *Jour. Exptl. Biol.,* **35:** 74–84.

MOHL, H. VON, 1851. *Grundzüge der Anatomie und Physiologie der vegetabilischen Zelle,* Braunschweig: Vieweg.

MOOSE, C. A., 1938. "Chemical and spectroscopic analysis of phloem exudate and parenchyma sap from several species of plants," *Plant Physiol.,* **13:** 365–380.

MÜNCH, E., 1927. "Versuche über den Saftkreislauf," *Ber. Deutsch. Bot. Ges.,* **45:** 340–356.

———, 1930. *Die Stoffbewegungen in der Pflanze,* Jena: Fischer.

NAGELI, C., 1861. "Ueber die Siebröhren von *Cucurbita,*" *Sitzungsber. Kgl. Bayer. Akad. der Wiss. zu München,* **1:** 212–238.

NELSON, C. D., and GORHAM, P. R., 1957. "Uptake and translocation of C^{14}-labeled sugars applied to primary leaves of soybean seedlings," *Can. Jour. Bot.,* **35:** 339–347.

———, PERKINS, H. J., and GORHAM, P. R., 1958. "Note on a rapid translocation of photosynthetically assimilated C^{14} out of the primary leaf of the young soybean plant," *Can. Jour. Bot.,* **36:** 1277–1279.

———, ———, ———, 1959. "Evidence for different kinds of concurrent translocation of photosynthetically assimilated C^{14} in the soybean," *Can. Jour. Bot.,* **37:** 1181–1189.

O'KELLEY, J. C., 1953. "The use of C^{14} in locating growth regions in the cell walls of elongating cotton fibers," *Plant Physiol.,* **28:** 281–286.

ORDIN, L., APPLEWHITE, T. H., and BONNER, J., 1956. "Auxin-induced water uptake by Avena coleoptile sections," *Plant Physiol.,* **31:** 44–53.

OSTERHOUT, W. J. V., 1922. "Some aspects of selective absorption," *Jour. Gen. Physiol.,* **5:** 225–230.

OVERSTREET, R., and JACOBSON, L., 1952. "Mechanisms of ion absorption by roots," *Ann. Rev. Plant Physiol.,* **3:** 189–206.

———, ———, and HANDLEY, R., 1952. "The effect of calcium on the absorption of potassium by barley roots," *Plant Physiol.,* **27:** 583–590.

OVERSTREET, R., RUBEN, S., and BROYER, T. C., 1940. "The absorption of bicarbonate ion by barley plants as indicated by studies with radioactive carbon," *Proc. Nat. Acad. Sci.,* **26:** 688–695.

PALLAS, J. E., JR., and CRAFTS, A. S., 1957. "Critical preparation of plant material for autoradiography," *Science,* **125:** 192–193.

PALMQUIST, E. M., 1939. "The path of fluorescein movement in the kidney bean, *Phaseolus vulgaris,*" *Amer. Jour. Bot.,* **26:** 665–667.

PERKINS, H. J., NELSON, C. D., and GORHAM, P. R., 1959. "A tissue-autoradiographic study of the translocation of C^{14}-labelled sugars in the stems of young soybean plants," *Can. Jour. Bot.,* **37:** 871–877.

PFEIFFER, M., 1937. "Die Verteilung der osmotischen Werte im Baum im Hinblick auf die Münchsche Druckstromtheorie," *Flora,* **132:** 1–47.

PHILIP, J. R., 1958. "The osmotic cell, solute diffusibility, and the plant water economy," *Plant Physiol.,* **33:** 264–271.

PHILLIS, E., and MASON, T. G., 1933. "The polar distribution of sugar in the foliage leaf," *Ann. Bot.,* **47:** 585–634.

PIERRE, W. H., and POHLMAN, G. G., 1933. "Preliminary studies of the exuded plant sap and the relation between the composition of the sap and the soil solution," *Jour. Amer. Soc. Agron.,* **25:** 144–160.

PRESTON, W. H., MITCHELL, J. W., and REEVE, W., 1954. "Movement of alpha-methoxyphenylacetic acid from one plant to another through their root systems," *Science,* **119:** 437–438.

PREVOT, P., and STEWARD, F. C., 1936. "Salient features of the root system relative to the problem of salt absorption," *Plant Physiol.,* **11:** 509–534.

PRIESTLEY, J. H., 1920. "The mechanism of root pressure," *New Phytol.,* **19:** 189–200.

———, 1929a. "Cell growth and cell division in the shoot of the flowering plant," *New Phytol.,* **28:** 54–81.

———, 1929b. "The transport of carbohydrates in the plant," *Nature,* **123:** 133–135.

RABIDEAU, G. S., and BURR, G. O., 1945. "The use of the C^{13} isotope as a tracer for transport studies in plants," *Amer. Jour. Bot.,* **32:** 349–356.

———, and MERICLE, L. W., 1953. "The distribution of C^{14} in the root and shoot apices of young corn plants," *Plant Physiol.,* **28:** 329–333.

REDISKE, J. H., and BIDDULPH, O., 1953. "The absorption and translocation of iron," *Plant Physiol.,* **28:** 576–593.

REDISKE, J. H., and SELDERS, A. A., 1953. "The absorption and translocation of strontium by plants," *Plant Physiol.*, **28:** 594–605.

RHODES, A., 1937. "The movement of fluorescein in the plant," *Leeds Philosoph. Soc. Proc.*, **3:** 389–395.

RICE, E. L., 1948. "Absorption and translocation of ammonium 2,4-dichlorophenoxyacetate by bean plants," *Bot. Gaz.*, **109:** 301–314.

———, and ROHRBAUGH, L. M., 1953. "Effect of kerosene on movement of 2,4-dichlorophenoxyacetic acid and some derivatives through destarched bean plants in darkness," *Bot. Gaz.*, **115:** 76–81.

———, ———, 1958. "Relation of potassium nutrition to the translocation of 2,4-dichlorophenoxyacetic acid in tomato plants," *Plant Physiol.*, **33:** 300–303.

ROECKL, BRUNHILD, 1949. "Nachweis eines Koncentrationshubs zwischen Palisadenzellen und Siebröhren," *Planta*, **36:** 530–550.

ROHRBAUGH, L. M., and RICE, E. L., 1949. "The effect of application of sugar on the translocation of sodium 2,4-dichlorophenoxyacetate by bean plants in the dark," *Bot. Gaz.*, **110:** 85–89.

———, ———, 1956. "Relation of phosphorus nutrition to the translocation of 2,4-dichlorophenoxyacetic acid in tomato plants," *Plant Physiol.*, **31:** 196–199.

ROMNEY, E. M., and TOTH, S. J., 1957. "Plant and soil studies with radioactive manganese," *Soil Sci.*, **77:** 107–117.

ROUSCHAL, ERNEST, 1941. "The protoplasmic mechanics and function of sieve tubes," *Flora*, **35:** 135–220.

RUHLAND, W., 1912. "Untersuchungen über den Kohlenhydratstoffwechsel von *Beta vulgaris* (Zuckerrube)," *Jahrb. Wiss. Bot.*, **50:** 200–255.

RUSSELL, E. J., 1927. *Soil conditions and plant growth,* London: Longmans, Green and Co.

RUSSELL, R. S., and SHORROCK, V. M., 1957. "The effect of transpiration on the absorption of inorganic ions by intact plants," *UNESCO Internatl. Conf. on Radioisotopes in Sci. Res. 1–15.* London: Pergamon Press.

SACHS, J., 1863. "Ueber die Leitung der plastischen Stoffe durch verschiedene Gewebeformen," *Flora*, **46:** 33–42; 49–58; 65–74.

———, 1882. *Textbook of Botany,* 2d ed., Oxford: Clarendon Press. Translation by S. H. Vines.

SCHIMPER, A. F. W., 1885. "Ueber Bildung und Wanderung der Kohlenhydrate in den Laubblattern," *Bot. Zeit.*, **48:** 737–743; 753–763; 769–787.

SCHMIDT, ERNEST WILLY, 1917. *Bau und Funktion der Siebröhre der Angiospermen*, Jena.

SCHOLANDER, P. F., LOVE, W. E., and KANWISHER, J. W., 1955. "The rise of sap in tall grapevines," *Plant Physiol.*, **30**: 93–104.

———, RUUD, B., and LEIVESTAD, H., 1957. "The rise of sap in a tropical liana," *Plant Physiol.*, **32**: 1–6.

SCHUMACHER, W., 1930. "Untersuchungen über die Lokalisation der Stoffwanderung in den Leitbundeln hoherer Pflanzen," *Jahrb. Wiss. Bot.*, **73**: 770–823.

———, 1933. "Untersuchungen über die Wanderung des Fluoreszeins in den Siebrohren," *Jahrb. Wiss. Bot.*, **77**: 685–732.

———, 1937. "Weitere Untersuchungen über die Wanderung von Farbstoffen in den Siebröhren," *Jahrb. Wiss. Bot.*, **85**: 422–449.

———, 1939. "Über die Plasmolysierbarkeit der Siebröhren," *Jahrb. Wiss. Bot.*, **88**: 545–553.

———, 1947. "Zur Frage nach den Stoffbewegungen im Pflanzenkörper," *Die Naturwiss.*, **6**: 176–179.

———, and HÜLSBRUCH, M., 1955. "Zur Frage dei Bewegung fluoreszierender Farbstoffe im Pflanzenkörper," *Planta*, **45**: 118–124.

SEVERIN, H. H. P., 1924. "Curly leaf transmission experiments," *Phytopath.*, **14**: 80–93.

SHALLA, T. A., 1960. Personal communication.

SHEETS, T. J., 1959. "The uptake, distribution and phytotoxicity of 2-chloro-4,6-bis(ethylamino)-s-triazine," Ph.D. thesis, University of California, Davis.

SISLER, R. M., DUGGER, W. M., JR., and GAUCH, H. C., 1956. "The role of boron in the translocation of organic compounds in plants," *Plant Physiol.*, **31**: 11–17.

SKOOG, F., 1938. "Absorption and translocation of auxin," *Amer. Jour. Bot.*, **25**: 361–372.

———, BROYER, T. C., and GROSSENBACHER, K. A., 1938. "Effects of auxin on rates, periodicity, and osmotic relations in exudation," *Amer. Jour. Bot.*, **25**: 749–759.

SPANNER, D. C., 1958. "The translocation of sugar in sieve tubes," *Jour. Exptl. Bot.*, **9**: 332–342.

STEWARD, F. C., 1935. "Mineral nutrition of plants," *Ann. Rev. Biochem.*, **4**: 519–544.

———, BERRY, W. E., and BROYER, T. C., 1936. "The absorption and accumulation of solutes by living plant cells," *Ann. Bot.*, **50**: 345–366.

STOREY, H. H., 1928. "Transmission studies of maize streak disease," *Ann. Appl. Biol.*, **15**: 1–25.

STOUT, M., 1945. "Translocation of the reproductive stimulus in sugar beets," *Bot. Gaz.*, **107**: 86–95.

Stout, P. R., and Hoagland, D. R., 1939. "Upward and lateral movement of salt in certain plants as indicated by radioactive isotopes of potassium, sodium, and phosphorus absorbed by roots," *Amer. Jour. Bot.*, **26:** 320–324.

Strasburger, Eduard, 1891. "Ueber den Bau und die Verrichtungen der Leitungsbahnen in den Pflanzen," *Histologische Beitrage 3,* Jena.

Swanson, C. A., 1957. "The translocation of organic nutrients in plants," AAAS publication, *Atomic energy and agriculture,* pp. 123–138.

———, and Böhning, R. H., 1951. "The effect of petiole temperature on the translocation of carbohydrates from bean leaves," *Plant Physiol.*, **26:** 557–564.

———, and Whitney, J. B., 1953. "Studies on the translocation of foliar-applied P^{32} and other radioisotopes in bean plants," *Amer. Jour. Bot.*, **40:** 816–823.

———, and El-Shishiny, E. D., 1958. "Translocation of sugars in the concord grape," *Plant Physiol.*, **33:** 33–37.

Swanson, C. P., 1946. "Histological responses of the kidney bean to aqueous sprays of 2,4-dichlorophenoxyacetic acid," *Bot. Gaz.*, **107:** 522–531.

Szent-Györgyi, A., 1956. "Bioenergetics," *Science,* **124:** 873–875.

Tammes, P. M. L., 1957. "Sieve tube sap," from a symposium, "Insect and Plant Food." Wageningen, Holland, May 27–29, 1957.

Thomas, W., 1927. "The seat of formation of amino acids in *Pyrus malus* L.," *Science,* n.s., **66:** 115–116.

Tingley, M. A., 1944. "Concentration gradients in plant exudates with reference to the mechanism of translocation," *Amer. Jour. Bot.*, **31:** 30–38.

Tolbert, N. E., and Zill, L. P., 1954. "Isolation of Carbon-14-labeled sedoheptulose and other products from *Sedum spectabile,*" *Plant Physiol.*, **29:** 288–292.

Ursprung, A., 1915. "Uber die Kohäsion des Wassers im Farnannulus," *Ber. Deutsch. Bot. Ges.*, **33:** 153–162.

Van den Honert, T. H., 1932. "On the mechanism of transport of organic materials in plants," *K. Akad. Wet. Amsterdam Proc.*, **35:** 1104–1112.

———, 1948. "Water transport in plants as a catenary process," *Faraday Soc. Disc.*, No. 3, pp. 146–153.

Vernon, L. P., and Aronoff, S., 1952. "Metabolism of soybean leaves. IV. Translocation from soybean leaves," *Arch. Biochem. and Biophys.*, **36:** 383–398.

VESQUE, J., 1884. "Recherches sur le mouvement de la sève ascendante," *Ann. des Sciences Nat. Bot.*, ser. vi, **19:** 159–199.

WALLIHAN, E. F., and HEYMANN-HERSCHBERG, L., 1956. "Some factors affecting absorption and translocation of zinc in citrus plants," *Plant Physiol.*, **31:** 294–299.

WANNER, H., 1953a. "Die Zusammensetzung des Siebröhrensaftes: Kohlenhydrate," *Ber. Schweiz. Bot. Ges.*, **63:** 162–168.

———, 1953b. "Enzyme der Glykolyse im Phloemsaft," *Ber. Schweiz. Bot. Ges.*, **63:** 201–212.

WEATHERLEY, P. E., PEEL, A. J., and HILL, G. P., 1959. "The physiology of the sieve tube. Preliminary experiments using aphid mouth parts," *Jour. Exptl. Bot.*, **10:** 1–16.

WEAVER, R. J., and DE ROSE, H. R., 1946. "Absorption and translocation of 2,4-dichlorophenoxyacetic acid," *Bot. Gaz.*, **107:** 509–521.

WEINTRAUB, R. L., and BROWN, J. W., 1950. "Translocation of exogenous growth-regulators in bean seedlings," *Plant Physiol.*, **25:** 140–149.

———, ———, FIELDS, M., and ROHAN, J., 1952. "Metabolism of 2,4-dichlorophenoxyacetic acid. I. $C^{14}O_2$ production by bean plants treated with 2,4-dichlorophenoxyacetic acids," *Plant Physiol.*, **27:** 293–301.

WENT, F. W., 1937. "Salt accumulation and polar transport of plant hormones," *Science*, **86:** 127–128.

———, 1944. "Plant growth under controlled conditions. III. Correlation between various physiological processes and growth in the tomato plant," *Amer. Jour. Bot.*, **31:** 597–618.

———, 1945. "Plant growth under controlled conditions. V. The relation between age, light, variety, and thermoperiodicity of tomatoes," *Amer. Jour. Bot.*, **32:** 469–479.

———, and ENGELSBERG, R., 1946. "Plant growth under controlled conditions. VIII. Sucrose content of the tomato plant," *Arch. Biochem.*, **9:** 187–200.

———, and HULL, H. M., 1949. "The effect of temperature upon translocation of carbohydrates in the tomato plant," *Plant Physiol.*, **24:** 505–526.

———, and THIMANN, K. V., 1937. *Phytohormones*. New York: Macmillan, 1937, 294 pages.

———, and WHITE, R., 1939. "Experiments on the transport of auxin," *Bot. Gaz.*, **100:** 465–484.

WESTERMAIER, M., 1883. "Zur Kenntniss der osmotischen Leistungen des lebenden Parenchyms," *Ber. Deutsch. Bot. Ges.*, **1:** 371–383.

WHALEY, W. G., MOLLENHAUER, H. H., and KEPHART, J. E., 1959. "The endoplasmic reticulum and the Golgi structures in maize root cells," *Jour. Biophys. and Biochem. Cytology*, **5:** 501–506.

———, ———, and LEECH, J. H., 1960. "The ultrastructure of the meristematic cell," *Amer. Jour. Bot.*, **47:** 401–450.

WHITE, P. R., 1938a. "Cultivation of excised roots of dicotyledonous plants," *Amer. Jour. Bot.*, **25:** 348–356.

———, 1938b. "Root pressure an unappreciated force in sap movement," *Amer. Jour. Bot.*, **25:** 223–227.

WIEBE, H. H., and KRAMER, P. J., 1954. "Translocation of radioactive isotopes from various regions of roots of barley seedlings," *Plant Physiol.*, **29:** 342–348.

WILLAM, A., 1945. "Translocation des glucides et origine du saccharose dans la betterave," *Inst. Belge pour l'Ameloir. de la Betterave*, P. **13:** 256–356.

WILLENBRINK, J., 1957. "Über die Hemmung des Stofftransports in den Siebröhren durch lokale Inaktivierung verschiedener Atmungenzyme," *Planta*, **48:** 269–342.

WISLICENUS, H., and HEMPEL, H., 1933. "Zur Kenntnis des stofflichen Aufbaues de Holzsubstanz aus den holzbilden den Saften der Baumpflanze," *Zellulosechemie*, **14:** 149–168.

WITHNER, C. L., 1949. "Movement of P^{32} in maturing corn plants," *Plant Physiol.*, **24:** 527–529.

WOODWARD, J., 1699. "Thoughts and experiments on vegetation," *Royal Soc. London Phil. Trans.*, **21:** 382–392.

WRIGHT, K. E., and BARTON, N. L., 1955. "Transpiration and the absorption and distribution of radioactive phosphorus in plants," *Plant Physiol.*, **30:** 386–388.

YAMAGUCHI, S., and CRAFTS, A. S., 1958. "Autoradiographic method for studying absorption and translocation of herbicides using C^{14}-labeled compounds," *Hilgardia*, **28:** 161–191.

ZACHARIAS, E., 1884. "Ueber den Inshalt der Siebröhren von *Cucurbita pepo*," *Bot. Zeit.*, **42:** 65–73.

ZECH, H., 1952. "Untersuchungen über den Infektionsvorgang und die Wanderung des Tobakmosaic-virus im Pflanzenkörpfer," *Planta*, **40:** 461–514.

ZIEGLER, H., 1956. "Untersuchungen über die Leitung und Sekretion der Assimilate," *Planta*, **47:** 447–500.

———, 1958. "Über die Atmung und den Stofftransport in den

isolierten Leitbundeln der Blattstiele von *Heracleum Mantegazzianum*," *Planta*, **51**: 186–200.

ZIMMERMANN, M. H., 1957a. "Translocation of organic substances in trees. I. The nature of the sugars in the sieve tube exudate of trees," *Plant Physiol.*, **32**: 288–291.

———, 1957b. "Translocation of organic substances in trees. II. On the translocation mechanism in the phloem of white ash (*Fraxinus americana* L.)," *Plant Physiol.*, **32**: 399–404.

———, 1958. "Translocation of organic substances in the phloem of trees," *The physiology of forest trees*, K. V. Thimann, ed., New York.

———, 1960. "Transport in the phloem," *Ann. Rev. Plant Physiol.*, **11**: 167–190.

index